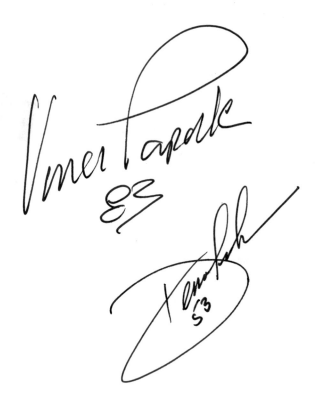

To Bill
You ARE INVINCIBLE

THE LAST LAUGH

VISION TO VICTORY

www.mascotbooks.com

The Last Laugh: Vision to Victory

Although the authors and publisher have made every effort to ensure that the information in this book was correct at press time, the author and publisher do not assume and hereby disclaim any liability to any party for any loss, damage, or disruption caused by errors or omissions, whether such errors or omissions result from negligence, accident, or any other cause. This book is not intended as a substitute for the medical advice of physicians. The reader should regularly consult a physician in matters relating to his/her health and particularly with respect to any symptoms that may require diagnosis or medical attention.

For more information, please contact:
Mascot Books
620 Herndon Parkway #320
Herndon, VA 20170
info@mascotbooks.com

CPSIA Code: PBANG0118A
Library of Congress Control Number: 2017918476
ISBN-13: 978-1-68401-615-0

Printed in the United States

THE LAST LAUGH

VISION TO VICTORY

DENNIS FRANKS   **VINCE PAPALE**

Table of Contents

We dedicate this book to our parents:

**Don and
Inge Franks**

&

**Almira and
Kingie Papale**

*You gave us the DNA for strength, speed, and
agility, but even more importantly, you passed
on the wisdom we needed to have our last laugh.*

No doubt we are among yours.

ACKNOWLEDGMENTS

Co-writer Bonnie Church worked tirelessly alongside us to conceptualize, develop, and write *The Last Laugh*. She has been a ghostwriter, contributing writer, journalist, and self-help columnist for more than thirty years. Dennis Franks mentored Bonnie and her husband, Michael, in their rise from "the creative underclass" to the world of successful entrepreneurship. Writing is now her side hustle. Matching people to the resources they need to live the life they want is her passion. Visit her at bonniechurch.com

DENNIS FRANKS

In success, there are always important people and influences that help form the mold that makes you. I acknowledge the following people for their support. To my amazing wife, Nancy, who has stood by my side throughout my post-football days and my entire business career, supporting my dreams and helping make them realities. My beautiful daughters, Lauren and Katie, who have made me proud throughout their lives, creating a new dimension to our thinking and existence. My parents, Don and Inge Franks, who have passed but have kept a special eye over me with their countless lessons and values by which I still live. Brother Don, an amazing example of intelligence and drive throughout his career, who showed me I could be so much more than a football player. Sister Claudia, for the many calls and letters of encouragement that made me feel like I could conquer the world. Your words and love will always be close to my heart. To my second parents and in-laws, Barb and Jim Haslett, your love and support has been a constant reminder to keep balance in my life. To my coaches—in high school, the late Rudy Andebaker; in college, the late Bo Schembechler; in the pros, Dick Vermeil and Monte Clark—a huge thank you for your discipline and values, which have influenced my life in and outside of football. Your teachings have stayed with me throughout the journey. To my good friend Kevin Buckman, "the professor"—so many miles we have traveled and so many learning experiences. My business partners of twenty-five years, JR Ridinger, Loren Ridinger, Marty Weissman, Marc Ashley, and Joe Bolyard—what an amazing learning curve to success! Finally, my hard-working assistant of twenty years, Yvonne—your love and caring for me kept me on schedule, making even the impossible days possible.

VINCE PAPALE

I am inspired everyday by "MY WHY": Janet, Gabby, and Vinny. To my Mom and Dad, Almira and Kingie, thanks for giving me the strength to chase my dream. I will always be grateful to these coaches and teachers for believing in me and my vision: George Corner, Dick Vermeil, Lou Nicastro, Marty Stern, and Kevin Quinn. I can't ever forget the thrill of being portrayed on the silver screen. Thanks to the All-Pro *Invincible* Team: Mark Wahlberg, Greg Kinnear, Elizabeth Banks, Ken Mok, Mark Ciardi, Gordon Gray, Brian Nguyen, and, of course, Walt Disney Productions.

Finally, a special thanks to all of those who doubted me: you provided me with the fuel to do the impossible.

FOREWORD

MARK WAHLBERG, *Academy Award-nominated actor and entrepreneur*

I'd grown up playing a lot of sandlot football, but until I had the opportunity to play the role of Vince Papale in the Disney film *Invincible*, I had never put the pads on. Once I was wearing number 83, I had the chance to step into a legend's shoes.

I love the underdog story, and I love the idea of the guy, the ordinary guy, doing something impossible. Vince has heart, and that's what inspired so many people and gave a city hope. That's why there isn't a person from Philadelphia, not a single Eagles fan, who doesn't know his name.

Dennis Franks, Vince's adversary turned best friend, has a dark horse story of his own. Rejected again and again by NFL teams, Dennis persisted, and his dedication eventually earned him a spot on the Eagles' roster, fulfilling his own NFL dream.

Bottom line: vision, hard work, and staying the course are more important than money, experience, and connections when it comes to success in sports and in life. With their extraordinary careers in both sports and business, Vince and Dennis are living proof of this.

The "Last Laugh" photo in the Pro Football Hall of Fame is a metaphor for overcoming the obstacles that stand between you and your goals. That is the story that Vince Papale and Dennis Franks live: the story of relentless overcomers. Whenever anything got them down—whether it was Vince's long road to the NFL or scouts insisting Dennis was too small to play in the NFL—both men engineered epic comebacks.

Wherever you are in your journey, and whatever it is that you're working toward, Vince and Dennis can teach you the fundamentals— how to work hard and have a heart that beats loud enough to drown out the naysayers.

For Vince and Dennis, it was all or nothing on the field. Now, they're going to give their all to you.

Are you ready to listen?

FOREWORD

CARL PETERSON, *former president, general manager, and CEO of the Kansas City Chiefs*

Reading *The Last Laugh* brought back some great memories. I was there to witness and admire Dennis Franks's and Vince Papale's efforts to overcome all obstacles and make an NFL team, the Philadelphia Eagles. The odds were stacked against them. Vince had no college football experience and Dennis lacked size, according to NFL standards.

Besides coaching the tight ends for the Philadelphia Eagles, I was in charge of running training camps. One of my most despised duties was being the bearer of bad news. I was the Turk. The Turk is the person who gets up early each morning, knocks on a player's door, and tells them to take their playbook to the head coach. This meant they were being cut and sent home—their dreams of playing in the NFL had ended. No one, especially Dennis and Vince, wanted to see me coming their way.

However, at training camp, I observed Dennis Franks's and Vince Papale's effort, energy, and enthusiasm in every drill and every practice. We played six preseason games in 1976 and their effort never wavered. They made the cut.

The Last Laugh includes their code of success, the Victor's Code. That code offers an excellent game plan and business plan for any endeavor. The proof in their formula of success is what they have each accomplished, not only on the football field but, more importantly, off the football field. Both have been very successful in their vocations. Both have experienced life's ups and downs, yet they have refused to stay down. In all the years that I have negotiated the waters of the National Football League, thirty-five plus years, I have never met two finer people.

In our business, we try to measure every statistic possible—height, weight, speed, agility, flexibility, and intelligence; but the one thing we cannot measure is the size of a man's heart. These two guys have big hearts, as big as anyone who has ever played in the National Football League. They have kept that same energy, excitement, and enthusiasm throughout their lives.

I've been to the Pro Football Hall of Fame in Canton, Ohio, to witness the induction of three of my former players. While there, I enjoyed taking a look at that great picture of Dennis and Vince getting the last laugh. It has been my pleasure to read this book and I highly recommend it to anyone and everyone.

INTRODUCTION:

THE LAST LAUGH

> *"What is most important to the heart of a warrior?*
> *The answer is, to desire with one's very soul every*
> *second of every day to accomplish one's aim."*

> **—Samurai Code**

It was 1976, the fourth game of the season. The Philadelphia Eagles were coming off a long run of mediocrity. It had been sixteen years since the last championship. All but the most die-hard fans had lost their zeal, but that was about to change. There was a new guy in town: Coach Dick

Vermeil. His goal was to take the Eagles to a position of prominence in the league and ultimately to the NFC Championship.

To strengthen our hope of going to the playoffs, we had to beat one of our biggest rivals: the Washington Redskins. Though the stands were packed with 70,000 people, not many were confident that the Eagles could win this game. The Skins were a scoring powerhouse, undefeated at that time.

That was the day we turned the tide.

The score by the fourth quarter was 17–14, our favor. We were vulnerable. We had a fourth down play and had to punt the ball from our 4 yard line, a little too close for comfort. With only one minute left on the clock, the pressure was on. It would not take much for the Redskins to get into field position to kick a field goal, tie the game, and take us into overtime.

Dennis, #53, came on as the offensive center and long snap for this play. Pressure was on him to deliver a perfect snap—the backwards pass to the punter who would kick the ball to the Redskins from the Eagles end zone—in under .75 seconds.

Dennis describes that moment:

I visualized a clean .7 second snap aimed at the right hip of the punter. This would ensure a perfect release. The stadium was loud and intense. The Washington Redskins defensive tackles were up in my face, trying to intimidate and distract me.

My hands were sweating. My grip was firm but comfortable. I looked through my legs and got the signal. The punter was ready; the snap was now on my count. With the flick of my wrists, I snapped the ball. It was spot on, and the punter released it downfield.

Vince, #83, bolted like he was shot out of a cannon. He escaped untouched from the line of scrimmage. He sprinted toward the Redskins' punt returner, who was eyeing the ball for a critical return. The Skins were hoping to tie the game or, at the very least, get good field position. From Vince's perspective:

As soon as the ball hit the hands of the punt returner, I crashed into him. I could hear the breath escaping his lungs as his body collapsed around my shoulder pad. The ball popped loose, and Dennis recovered the fumble. The game was ours. We won our first big game of the season, and against the undefeated Washington Redskins.

We not only won the game; we won back the hearts of Eagles fans everywhere. The Philadelphia Eagles proved worthy of competing for the NFC Championship that year. Three years later, they played in Super Bowl XV.

That photo of us laughing our asses off and celebrating our hard-won victory was captured that day. It precisely expresses the emotion we felt when, against all odds and in the face of naysayers, pain, and self-doubt, we did it! The "Last Laugh" photo now hangs in the Pro Football Hall of Fame in Canton, Ohio.

Our struggle against seemingly impossible odds didn't end on the field. We have scored some victories in business, too. We share some of those in section two, "The Rest of the Story."

The same enemies that pursued us in our athletic careers pursued us in our business endeavors. We experienced betrayal, mistakes of the past coming back to haunt us, financial hard times, health crises, and discouragement, but we didn't quit. Even today, when others from our generation are focused on retiring, we are wired for more action.

Our success isn't because of our abilities alone. Let's face it: there are a lot of talented people in the world who don't succeed. Our victories came from our commitment to identify and apply the fundamentals of success to everything we set out to do. We call those fundamentals the Victor's Code.

Our goal is to help you "crack the code" of victory and apply it to your life. We'll unpack it step by step. Whether you want to score in sports, learn how to fly a plane, lose weight, launch a business, beat cancer, write a book, you name it, a commitment to the Victor's Code will help get you there.

The Last Laugh's "Hall of Fame" (section three) will give you a seat at the table with other successful people as they share how the Victor's Code shaped their journey. Like us, their goal is to provide inspiration and mentorship to you as you discover how to apply the code to your journey toward personal victory.

SECTION I:

THE VICTOR'S CODE

"Far better is it to dare mighty things, to win glorious triumphs, even though checkered by failure, than to rank with those poor spirits who neither enjoy nor suffer much, because they live in the gray twilight that knows not victory nor defeat."

—Theodore Roosevelt

There are universal fundamentals that undergird every great achievement. Those fundamentals help you figure out where you want to go in life and provide a map for getting there.

We have identified seven timeless universals in the Victor's Code. This code is all the magical pieces that cracked the code of victory; it's something we discovered. This code is written on the bottoms of our feet and embedded deep in our souls. When we have strayed from its wisdom, we have suffered the consequences. When we have adhered to it, we have enjoyed a continuous flow of last laughs. Our passion is to share the Victor's Code with you.

The saying goes, "Pass the truth to the next generation. Teach them early what we learn late." If you are just starting out in life, we are passing the baton of truth to you in the hope that it will shorten your learning curve considerably. Learn it, internalize it, and enjoy the journey.

For those of you who've lived some years but still have unmet desires and goals, it's never too late. The Victor's Code might not be new to you; perhaps you've heard it before, or maybe you even lived by it at one time. Our encouragement to you? Blow the dust off your bucket list and apply the code afresh.

Are you with us?

Let's get started.

VISION:

THE STATE OF BEING ABLE TO SEE

"Vision is the art of seeing what is invisible to others."

—Jonathan Swift

The key to living your best life begins with a dream. We all have them:

- The house you want to live in
- The car you want to drive
- The business you want to launch
- The causes you want to support
- The body you want
- The toys you want
- Finding the love of your life
- Making the cut on your dream team

Bottom line: your dream is your utopian world. A vision is your dream in high definition.

Think of your dream as a flashlight pointing in the general direction of what you want. Vision, on the other hand, is a laser beam. It's clear. It's compelling. It's so compelling, in fact, that it shuts out all other distractions. It encompasses where you want to go and what it feels like and looks like to get there.

An Olympic gymnast nails the dismount before she steps into the arena. A pro golfer lands the shot before he swings the club. A star batter knocks the ball out the park before it leaves the pitcher's hand. A successful entrepreneur cashes that million-dollar check before she's made a penny. They envision it before it happens.

Once you're clear on what you want to accomplish, it's time to hustle. Hustle is the price you pay to make your dreams come true. Songwriter Joel Baker sums it up beautifully: "Vision without action is a dream. Action without vision is simply passing the time." Here's one example of how the envisioning process worked in our lives.

We shared a common dream to play in the NFL. Against the odds, we made the team. Great start, but we wanted more. We wanted to be valuable members of the Philadelphia Eagles franchise. We had to prove to Coach Vermeil that he made the right choice. To play at a respectable level in pro ball requires more than a playbook—it requires a clear vision of what you want to accomplish and a no-holds-barred determination to get it done.

We were part of the offense and special teams. That meant we had multiple jobs to do. On offense, our goal was to get the ball into the end zone. At the very least, we needed to score points every time we possessed the ball.

We played on a variety of special teams: kickoff, kickoff return, onside kick (a.k.a. hands team), punt, punt return, field goal, and extra point plays were all familiar territory. The more you could do, the more valuable you were to the team and the longer you could stay in the game.

We were known for our craziness and especially loved being part of the kickoff and kickoff return teams. These teams set the tempo of the game. Every kickoff or kickoff return was like an explosion—definitely not for the faint of heart. It looked like a car wreck from the stands, but those plays were a result of clear-cut strategies and tactics.

Our special teams coach, Ken Iman, printed "Who's Nuts" t-shirts that would be awarded to the player who made the biggest hit of the game. In the hotel room the night before every game, laughing like a couple of goofballs, we would plan our big hits. We envisioned doing crazy things on the field. We would play every snap as though it were our last. Unbridled joy! We earned a suitcase full of those t-shirts.

One kickoff return play was called a "wedge." The wedge was like a snow plow consisting of four huge guys weighing between 275 and 300 pounds. That mass of flesh and bone would lock arms and advance at full gallop toward the defensemen to plow a path for the ball carrier. The wedge would smash anyone who attempted to tackle the ball carrier. It was a strategy meant to intimidate and crush the opposition. This bold play had the potential to inflict serious harm. That's why it's no longer legal.

Crazy. We know. But we loved breaking the wedge. We would visualize running full-on toward it. Dennis would take out two or more of the wedge blockers. Vince would propel himself over the human mass and make a tackle. In our minds, we were the master wedge-busters of the NFL. Unlike some of our other goals in life, this one, if not executed properly, could result in some serious injuries.

Our wedge-busting strategy began with vision. Dennis envisioned himself as an Army tank. The whistle would blow, the kicker kicked the ball, and off Dennis surged, full speed ahead, indestructible, mowing down the encroaching opposition. Vince envisioned himself as a cheetah, the fastest animal on earth, vaulting over the broken wedge and making the tackle.

As we created these compelling visions, it affected us physically: Dennis optimized his strength, first in his tank vision and then in his body. He was unstoppable. Vince, after so much time spent visualizing the agility of the cheetah, became faster. Our minds paved the way for us to create our reality. We physically felt the shift as our bodies lined up with our visions. Seeing it in our minds' eyes gave us the edge to excel, and we were damn good at breaking wedges because of it.

The mind has a powerful effect on the body. Placebo painkillers—sugar pills—have been shown to trigger the release of natural pain-relieving chemicals called endorphins. One article in *Scientific American* references a study involving the outcome of placebo consumption for patients with Parkinson's disease.[1] Subjects who took a placebo experienced a flood of dopamine. In other words, merely believing they were taking a medication that would help them stimulated their bodies to produce a change. This is called the placebo effect.

A similar thing happens when you get very clear on what you want to accomplish—so clear that you can see it; you can feel it. Something happens in your brain and that thing that seemed impossible begins to clarify. You start doing the things that need to be done to get you to your goal. The closer you get, the more motivated you become. You chomp at the bit to close the deal.

Some of us are better at vision than others. You might not be among those able to conjure powerful mental images easily. That's okay. The process of transforming your dreams into a compelling, reality-based vision can be learned. We're here to guide you through that process.

First, you'll need a chunk of distraction-free time—a "dream-conjuring getaway," so to speak. Put it on your calendar. Schedule an entire day or two if possible. During your getaway, you will work through the following steps. Be sure to take a notebook and pen. Laptops are okay but can lead to vision-interrupting distractions.

Get into dream mode. Find a comfortable chair, grab your favorite beverage, and let your mind go. For some of us, we think more clearly and creatively on our feet. That's fine, too. Take a walk, work out, whatever works. Your vision will become the guiding force in your life. It's worth investing your time to find it. If you don't take time to clarify your vision, you'll flounder right out of the gate.

The Seven Step Process

STEP ONE: WHAT DO I WANT?

Once locked into dream mode, make a list of everything you would like to achieve before you die. It's sometimes called a bucket list. Be daring. Don't worry about the price tag yet—you'll vet your list with a reality check later. Now is the time to just dream.

Everyone's bucket list is different. For some, it might be learning how to play guitar. For others, it might be climbing Mount Everest. Some want a tiny cabin in the Adirondacks; others want a 1,000-acre ranch in Utah or a beach house in Malibu. Some want to launch a new business; others want a promotion at work. Some want to lose a few pounds; others want to try out for the Olympics. It's about you and what you want.

A good way to kick into dreaming mode is to think about someone you admire, someone who has what you want.

Dennis's desire to become a professional athlete began in elementary school. Jimmy Kelly, a neighbor, played football at Clairton High School in Pennsylvania. Jimmy lived in a row home on Connecticut Avenue, four doors down from the Franks, and received a full athletic scholarship to the University of Notre Dame. He was the talk of the town and Dennis's hero:

My dream was to be like him. I envisioned myself playing football in high school and getting a scholarship to play in college.

One day, Jimmy drove up the alley behind the row houses in a brand-new burgundy Bonneville he had purchased with his draft bonus after signing with the Pittsburgh Steelers.

Wow! My dream got bigger. Jimmy Kelly showed me that a kid from Clairton could make it in the pros. I wanted to be just like him. I wanted to have what he had. I was going to play in the NFL.

Coincidentally, Jimmy Kelly finished his career with the Philadelphia Eagles, making us fellow Philadelphia Eagles Alumni. At a recent alumni gathering, Dennis had an opportunity to share with Jimmy's grandsons how their grandfather inspired him to go for his dream.

Vince's dream was inspired by wide receiver Tommy McDonald. McDonald was just 5'9" and only 176 pounds, but he was a giant on the field. He was rarely hurt because no one could catch him, and if they did hurt him, it didn't stop him. He was tough, fast, fearless, and cocky.

After games, I would pretend to be Tommy McDonald. I'd lie on the living room floor, throw a football into the air, and try to roll over and catch it before it hit the ground—just like Tommy did. McDonald wore Riddell cleats, so I had to wear Riddell cleats. He wore a helmet without a face mask, so I wanted to wear a helmet without a face mask. He would sandpaper his fingertips before games to make them more sensitive. I planned to do that, too. I like the way he talked and walked and ran. I liked the way he caught the ball. I had a vision of being McDonald. I was going to play wide receiver for the Eagles.

The rest is history.

There is no right or wrong way to create your bucket list. It can be as detailed and descriptive as you want. Just keep writing until you have exhausted the possibilities.

It's YOUR dream. Have at it.

STEP TWO: WHAT DO I NOT WANT?

Let's shift gears now. There's a lot of talk about the power of positive thinking. You know the philosophy—if you think hard enough and long enough, your brain will figure out a way to achieve it. But what about the power of negative thinking? What about the power of pain?

Look at each item on your bucket list. Take some time to think about what life will be like if you don't reach that goal. Envision what life will be like if your waistline continues to grow, your income continues to shrink, or that business deal doesn't come through.

Is the thought painful to you? If not, then you are unlikely to sustain the energy needed to achieve it. If it's "no biggie," take it off your list.

STEP THREE: WHAT DO I REALLY, REALLY, REALLY WANT?

Let's whittle the list down even further. Review each of the remaining items on your bucket list and ask yourself the questions below. There are only two answers: yes or no. Maybe is not an option. A maybe is a no.

- Do I believe this is possible for ME to achieve?
- Do I have a strong desire to achieve this?
- Is the timing right?
- Am I ready to find/invest in the resources needed?
- Am I willing to create and commit to an action plan?

The items that you answer "100% Yes!" represent your goals. The sum total of those goals is the big picture—your vision. Write these items on a new list. They made the final cut.

Congratulations! You have just created a compelling list of things you want to accomplish. It's okay if you ended up with only one or two things. Laser-focusing on a few goals is better than getting overwhelmed and off-track by having too many.

STEP FOUR: HOW DO I GET IT?

Answer the questions below for each goal. The answers will give you the information you need to develop an action plan.

- What daily disciplines will I need to practice?

- How much money do I need to save or raise?
- What new skills do I need to learn?
- What other resources do I need?
- What associations/relationships do I need to cultivate?
- What will a day in my life look like?

Having trouble answering these questions? A great short cut is to ask someone who has done what you want to do. Schedule a time to interview them and ask those questions. Most successful people, if they have the time, are willing to share what they have learned. Another option is to read books and listen to podcasts relevant to your goals.

STEP FIVE: WHEN DO I WANT IT?

Create a timeline for achievement. Set a deadline for each goal. Make it realistic. Identify the sub-goals that serve your end goal. Set deadlines for them—this will help you stay on track.

EXAMPLE: *Let's say you're out of shape, but you dream of running the Boston Marathon. Working with a trainer, you've identified other goals that need to be reached before you buy that ticket to Boston. Your couch-to-marathon journey might look like this.*

GOAL:
Boston Marathon – 2019 (2 years)

SUB-GOALS:
1st month—Fast-walk 3 miles
3rd month—Run 5k
12th month—Run/walk half marathon
18th month—Run half marathon
24th month—Boston Marathon, I am on my way!

STEP SIX: WHAT DOES IT FEEL LIKE TO ACHIEVE MY VISION?

Vision is not something mystical and distant. You must envision yourself there NOW! Committing your goals to paper and reviewing them daily will provide the motivation you need to stay the course. It will give you that tap on the shoulder (or kick in the pants) when you slack off. *Hey guy. Look around. You're not there yet. Get back to work.*

Write out a statement for each goal in the present tense. Make it as descriptive as you can (but don't let your lack of poetic ability stop you).

EXAMPLE: *It's 2025. I'm waking up in my eight-bedroom beach house in Malibu. I'm going for a morning swim, followed by a delicious, healthy breakfast prepared by our gourmet chef. I will enjoy breakfast with the love of my life. Our marriage is better than ever. We're having a relaxed conversation about our future under our vine-draped pergola, surrounded by beautiful gardens.*

EXAMPLE: *I am crossing the finish line at the 2020 Boston Marathon. I hear the cheers of my friends who are lined up to see me finish. The sweat is pouring down my face. I feel energized and victorious. I made it!*

If words aren't your thing, create a vision board. Find pictures in magazines, brochures, or online that depict each of your goals. Paste them to a poster board with your dates for achievement. Not crafty? No problem: find pictures and save them to a gallery on your phone or computer. These pictures will keep your dream alive. They will trigger the emotional and mental experience of what attaining your dream will feel like.

Actor and comedian Jim Carrey envisioned becoming a millionaire. In 1990, the struggling, almost-penniless young comic wrote himself a check for $10,000,000. He put in the notation line, "For acting services rendered," dated it Thanksgiving, 1995, and stuck it in his wallet. By 1995, Carrey had starred in *Ace Ventura, Pet Detective*; *The Mask*; and *Liar, Liar*. His per film fee? $20 million.

Start your day by reading your statement or looking at your vision board. See yourself doing the stuff necessary to make each goal a reality.

STEP SEVEN: WHAT IF THINGS DON'T GO AS PLANNED?

Sometimes circumstances shift: obstacles and opportunities present themselves in equal measure. You need to be flexible and adjust course to accommodate these changing conditions.

- Analyze those opportunities and obstacles.
- Adapt to them.
- Achieve despite or because of them.

In football, we describe it as "calling an audible."

In *Invincible*, there's a scene that depicts a successful audible. Dennis demonstrates to Vince how to read the stance of an opposing player. "Read the knuckles!" he says. The knuckles predict the weight displacement of an opponent. Weight on, the knuckles become a bloodless white or ashy color. This means the opposition is positioned to charge directly at you. Weight off, the blood comes back and the knuckles darken to a reddish color. The opposition is positioned to angle around you.

That "read the knuckles" tip changed the course of one pivotal game. The Eagles were playing the Giants and the score was tied 14–14. At the line of scrimmage, Vince noticed the cover man's knuckles were white. He was positioned to hit Vince at the line of scrimmage.

Vince called an audible and changed the play to Check Zorro. He sprinted to the punt returner and made a great hit. The punt returner fumbled the ball, and Vince grabbed it and raced to score the winning touchdown. The Eagles' losing streak was broken. In the movie, Coach Vermeil says, "Now that's the sound we've been looking for."

That is the impact of a well-called audible. It can change the course of a football game or the course of your life. When confronted with new opportunities or obstacles, Triple A it.

- Analyze those opportunities and obstacles (Read the knuckles!).
- Adapt to them (Check Zorro).
- Achieve despite or because of them (Touchdown!).

Sometimes you're not the one to call the audible. It's in the hands of someone else and you must adjust.

Dennis was recruited to play linebacker for the Michigan Wolverines—his dream position. The plan was to team up with linebacker Steve Strinko—a big guy with brains and talent. This was going to be a tandem made in heaven.

Then suddenly my best laid plans fell apart. Coach Bo Schem-bechler decided to move me to offensive center. What? Linebackers stand and run. Centers crouch and block. It meant learning a whole new skill set: how to snap the ball, call blocking schemes, and implement blocking assignments. This meant starting at the bottom and working my way up the chain of command. I was not happy. I strongly considered leaving the team.

Dennis eventually accepted his fate. He learned the new position and eventually loved it. As offensive center, he helped Michigan win three Big Ten championships.

Sometimes you don't like the audible that has been called. Sometimes it messes with your plans. Roll with it. Don't give up on your dreams. That audible just might open doors that lead to some of your heartiest last laughs.

VALOR:

POSSESSING EXCEPTIONAL COURAGE AND DETERMINATION

"The Spartans do not ask how many are the enemy, but where they are."

—Plutarch

When we think of courage, we think of people willing to put themselves in harm's way to do what is right: Martin Luther King Jr. protesting for equal rights; Charles Lindbergh making the first nonstop flight from New York to Paris; Sir Edmund Hillary, the first to climb Mount Everest; the Navy Seals who raided Osama Bin Laden's compound; airline Captain "Sully" Sullenberger, who safely landed a disabled US Airways flight on the Hudson river, saving the 155 people on board. People like that.

Those are exceptional acts of courage and they deserve our admiration. Most of us are not called upon to demonstrate that level of courage. We are not going to be asked to rush into a burning building to save a child, stand up to terrorists, or walk a tight rope over Niagara Falls.

However, if you are committed to fulfilling your vision, you are going to be called upon to leave your comfort zone. You are going to be asked to dive into the unknown with no guarantees of success. You are going to have to be willing to get out of prep mode and take action.

There is a cost for taking courageous measures. Yes, you might fail. People might call you a fool. But there is a greater cost if you linger on the sidelines. Fear can cost you your hopes and dreams.

If not killed, fear—like cancer—will sabotage your goals and destroy your health. Here's the short list of problems uncontrolled fear can create: diminished immune system performance, digestive problems, teeth grinding, headaches, high blood pressure, edginess, depression, insomnia, fatigue, memory and concentration issues, over-eating or under-eating, and the use of recreational drugs.

It also wreaks havoc on relationships. The irritability triggered by fear and its cousin anxiety destroys your ability to be the friend and lover we all long to be.

How do you know you are fear-driven? Here are some signs:

▫ You obsessively think about the regrets of yesterday and the threats of tomorrow. When life is good, you can't enjoy it because you are always waiting for the other shoe to drop.

▫ You stay in your comfort zone—both physically and emotionally. You rationalize: *If I don't venture out, I won't get hurt.* Vince was told that it was too risky to try out for the Eagles, that he was too old and inexperienced. Dennis was told he was too small to be a center. Imagine if we believed those indictments and allowed them to imprison us in our respective comfort zones.

▫ You are fatalistic. You assume the worst and that gives you a justification to not even try: *Why try? It is not going to work anyway.*

▫ You fixate on mistakes and beat yourself up. Instead of seeing the 95% successful result, you focus on the 5% that didn't quite work out as planned. The naysayer will surely focus on your 5%, won't they? After every NFL game, there was a film review. *The camera don't lie.* Even if we played a great game but messed up one play, we dreaded the film. The bad play would pop up for all to see. The coach would rip us a new one in front of the team. Mistakes are part of the game. The sooner you accept that, the better off you'll be.

▫ You procrastinate. Instead of taking action, you read books about taking action. You wait until circumstances are perfect before acting. (Here's a hint: they never are.)

- You don't finish what you start. You rationalize: *If I don't finish it, no one can judge it.*

- You apologize for yourself. *If I play small, if I lower expectations, people will be less disappointed if I fail and will be pleasantly surprised if I succeed.* That's the attitude for the average Joe, and that is not what you're about, or you wouldn't be reading this book!

- You resist accountability out of fear that if people look too closely they will see flaws. In the NFL, we were held to the highest level of scrutiny. We not only had to rise to our own expectations, but also to those of our coaches, fans, and teammates.

- You're a workaholic. You fear that if you slow down for even a moment, poverty or the negative opinions of others will catch you. This can destroy your health and rob your family of what they want most—time with you.

- You are addicted to drugs or alcohol. Nothing numbs fear like getting sloshed.

Yes, many fears are overblown and imagined, but there are some real threats to your health and wellbeing. What do you do about those?

A very real threat we faced in the NFL was doing serious damage to our bodies. Oh yes—we're talking concussions and broken bones. We were known for wedge-busting—that massive four-man snow plow determined to intimidate and crush us.

To overcome our very real fear of being flattened by the wedge, we took a sober assessment of the threats (the wedge), took an inventory of our resources (agility, strength, and courage), and devised a plan of attack. Dennis would go low and run toward the point of the wedge, screaming a war cry. Vince would vault the wedge to get to the ball carrier. We usually succeeded.

We don't recommend that any of you intentionally put yourself in the path of a wedge, but you get the point. There was a very real possibility of getting hurt, but we were willing to take the risk. We weren't stupid (Okay. Some might argue with that); we took precautions against getting flattened.

There are real wedges to face in your life. The tactics for protecting yourself are the same.

- Identify the threat.
- Assess your resources.
- Develop a strategy for overcoming.

The real threats are easier to cope with than the pervasive, under-the-surface, imagined threats. They can be the hardest to resolve because they're so tied up with our emotions. Look at it this way.

Fear =

False

Evidence

Appearing

Real.

Fear is a paper tiger. It looks fierce, but it's paper thin. You could poke a hole through it with your pinky. You could rip it to shreds with your bare hands.

Yet, that tiger roars:

If you fail, you are going to be a big disappointment to your spouse, your kids, and your friends.

If you fail, people will think you are a fool.

If you fail, people will reject you.

That roar can stop you in your tracks. So how do you shut it up? Here are some proven tactics that can help you manage your fear.

DO A REALITY CHECK.

We don't mind flying in airplanes, but we're not the norm. Flying happens to be one of the most common fears and anxieties, right up there with public speaking (we're not scared of that, either).

Dennis was once on a turbulent flight with his close friend, Kevin Buckman. Kevin was obviously uneasy, so Dennis offered some reassurance: "If we go down, Kevin, it's up to the Universe, air traffic control, and the pilot to take care us. If it's our time, it's our time."

Kevin, not particularly reassured, said, "Hey—what if it's not my time, but it's the time of the guy in that seat over there?" Wow. That was right up there with one of the most creative fear justifications we've ever heard.

These are the facts behind those fears, and you should rest in them: An American has a 1 in 11 million chance of dying in a plane crash, but a 1 in only 5,000 chance of dying in a car accident. Is that going to stop you from driving? The nation would grind to a halt. (By the way, the likelihood of dying on stage during a public speaking gig is pretty low, too.) Keep your fears in perspective. Most of them are wildly out of line with reality.

There is an old saying: *I've seen a lot of trouble in my time, and most of it never happened.* Think about it. How many days have you wasted worrying about things that never happened? Or, if they did, when was the outcome as horrible as anticipated?

CALCULATE THE COST OF FEAR.

The human brain is wired to fear risk. We don't like to make ourselves vulnerable to threats. Yes—sometimes it is easier to "play it safe." But cowardice has its cost. It can mean sacrificing your dreams.

Vince was told he was too old and inexperienced for pro ball. He was vulnerable to injuries. To give into those fears of potential bodily harm would mean sacrificing his dream. That was too big a price to pay.

FEED YOUR MIND WITH GOOD STUFF.

Read self-help books and blogs. Listen to uplifting podcasts. Listen to testimonials from people just like you who faced their fears, overcame them, and succeeded. They don't call it en-COURAGE-ment for nothing. Hearing other peoples' stories will give you courage.

CLARIFY YOUR REASON WHY.

Remind yourself that succeeding in your business is about taking care of your family. Losing weight or fighting a cancer prognosis is about living a healthy life so you can fulfill your purpose. Without a WHY, fear of dying, fear of failure, fear of rejection, and all those other "False Evidences that Appear Real" will devour you. With a WHY, you're tiger-proof.

MANAGE YOUR STRESS.

Worry triggers the release of a hormone called cortisol. Cortisol is useful for giving you the energy you need for a short-term crisis (think fight or flight response), but if you continually soak in it, it will break you down—mind, body, and soul. Learn some techniques for managing your stress. We'll give you some tips on that later.

SURROUND YOURSELF WITH LIKEMINDED PEOPLE.

There is a saying, *If you can't change the people you are with, change the people you are with.* If you are hanging out with naysayers and downers, it's time to find some new friends. Hanging out with positive-minded people who have similar goals creates a comradery and a fearlessness by association. Seminars, networking events, and support groups are a great place to discover new friends.

FEEL THE FEAR AND DO IT ANYWAY.

And what if you take a risk and fail? So what? Failure is just feedback. It's not a personal indictment. It's the information you need to get up, try again, and do it better this time.

Market America, Dennis's company, started their international launch in Australia several years ago. They did the homework, but there were still a lot of unknowns. That didn't stop them. They launched. There were challenges to face and mistakes made, but they did it. Fifteen years later, Market Australia continues to thrive and Market America has opened new markets in Europe, Asia, and North America.

GET IN FOCUS MODE.

According to the *Mayo Guide on Stress-free Living*, when you're laser-focused on a conversation or a project, a constellation of neurons in your brain called the task-positive network engage.[2] You fall into a state of cheerful forgetfulness and anxiety is reduced. Instead of worrying about how well your book is going to be received by the critics, lock in and focus on writing. Instead of worrying about all the things that could go wrong with your business ideas, immerse yourself in your project.

GO FOR IT. TRYING (TAKING ACTION) IS A WIN.

As the saying goes, *Better to have tried and failed than never to have tried at all.* World-class boxer George Foreman was told he was crazy to fight Michael Moorer, a boxer twenty years his junior. Foreman wasn't worried about the outcome. His philosophy? "I'm a winner every time I go into the ring." He won that fight and a place in the Boxing Hall of Fame.

GET HELP IF YOU NEED IT.

You might be wracked with fear and that fear is keeping you from reaching your goals. The tips we've provided here are to help conquer the fears and anxieties that are holding you in place. If you think your fear is more deep-seated or if it is making you incapable of working or maintaining your relationships and wellbeing, see a mental health professional. There's no shame in taking a step that could help you live a better life.

Paper tigers, you're going down!

VEHEMENCE:

SHOWING GREAT ENERGY OR PASSION

"When your desires are strong enough, you will appear to possess superhuman powers to achieve."

—Napoleon Hill

Water heated to 211 degrees Fahrenheit is hot. It might even bubble a little. But when you add just one degree, it boils. That's what vehemence is—that extra degree that will take you from 211 to 212 degrees. That extra degree creates the heat you need to get out of the gate. Just like one of those old steam engines, you are not going to sustain the steam you need to fulfill your vision without heat. Vehemence is the boiling point.

Here are some ways to increase your vehemence.

FIRE-STOKING RITUALS

MORNING RITUALS

What you do in the first hour of your day sets the tone for the other twenty-three. These activities vary widely, but many successful people launch their day with a ritual.

- Success guru Tony Robbins takes a cold plunge into a pool. He primes his mind through affirmations and power statements.

- Four-hour work week guru Tim Ferris has a practice called Morning Pages—three pages of stream-of-consciousness writing without judgement. This ritual primes the creative juices.

- Dennis drinks a potent vitamin cocktail and dives into phone-free exercise (just like normal exercise, but without the distraction of a mobile device). This clears and focuses his mind to attack the day.

- Vince's favorite way to meet the day is to walk out on the back deck of his house, take a deep breath, listen to the sweet voices of nature around him, and think about how grateful he is for all he has.

Some take a brisk walk with an inspiring podcast, some meditate, some pray. Whatever your method, morning rituals set your course early. They keep you from being derailed by moods, busywork, naysayers, and other distractions. A morning ritual will set your feet on a well-worn path that will keep you heading in the direction of your goals.

GAME DAY RITUALS

As professional jocks, game day rituals kept us fired up and focused. We channeled the spirit of ancient Roman gladiators preparing to enter the coliseum and fight to the death. But whether you are slated to perform on a field, on stage, or in the office, rituals prime you for action. This is what we did before Eagles games, rain or shine:

First light, we're awake. No need for an alarm. We envision clearly what we want to accomplish and we are primed to make it happen. Breakfast at 9 a.m.; kickoff at 1 p.m. sharp.

We race to the stadium wearing our lucky baseball hats. We walk the empty field and imagine the stands filled with cheering fans. We can feel the ball being snapped and carried. When the whistle blows, the ball is kicked and play begins like lighting a stick of dynamite. The length of time it takes to run down the field is how long the wick burns. Bodies collide in a huge explosion. The fans hold their breath or groan or cheer depending on the outcome. We envision it all. We're jazzed and ready for action.

Then, in the locker room, the trainers tape our wrists and ankles. The taping ritual fuels our confidence. The tightness of the tape makes us feel superhuman and ready to make contact with the opposition.

We stretch. We put on our equipment in a certain order, individual to each player. We wear the right t-shirt, the right socks. We adjust the snugness of our shoulder pads and perfectly position our leg pads and rib protectors. We are fearless.

We're not smokers, but we take a buzzworthy drag on a cigarette before every game to get that nicotine edge. Then we sit staring at each other in full uniform, our legs bouncing up and down like a room full of kids who have to pee.

We no longer play ball, but we still have "game day" rituals. The stage is now our field. The impact we make is on minds, not bodies. We take that shower, we slap on that aftershave, and put on our uniforms—business casual or custom-fitted suits and Italian leather. Whatever the occasion demands.

Visualization is an important part of the game day ritual. We envision ourselves entering the stage and connecting with the audience. We mentally rehearse our presentation from kickoff to conclusion.

Dennis launches his presentation with a high-energy entrance to chest-pounding techno music. That ritual stokes him and it stokes the audience.

Vince describes his own pregame ritual:

I knew after the movie and first book came out that I would be a public speaker. I saw it clearly: myself as a public speaker, and a damn good one. An effective public speaker can't fumble. Every time you're on stage, it's the Super Bowl. Coach Vermeil used to drive home the importance of setting the tempo of the game. Before every speaking engagement, I go to a quiet spot. I close my eyes and imagine the first three minutes of my presentation and how I am going to set the tempo.

SOUL-FEEDING RITUALS

The trend these days is to post selfies on social media to show people when you're at your best. (Hey, maybe even to create a little envy!) That's all in good fun, but sometimes the camera should be pointed away from us and focused on others who are bravely enduring challenges we can only imagine.

During our Eagles years, before we hit the bar to watch Monday Night Football, we would visit patients at a burn center near Veterans Stadium. Then we would sneak into the Children's Hospital of Philadelphia to cheer up the kids suffering from leukemia. No TV cameras in our faces, the press wasn't there to report on how great we were, we were just there for the kids.

We received far more than we gave from these evenings with those kids. Talk about a lesson in valor! We were inspired by the courage of the burn patients and the kids battling leukemia. Based on the statistics of the time, 80% of leukemia sufferers—80% of the kids we met—would not survive.

It sure put things in perspective. What we had to endure to reach our goals was insignificant compared to their heroism and bravery. Those visits grounded us and cultivated gratitude for our lives. It made our personal pain no big deal.

One day, cancer came knocking on our door. Both of us lost parents to cancer. Vince had his own battle. He got that call from a doc that nobody wants: "Vince, are you sitting down? I've got some bad news for you. You've got cancer." Our ability to walk through that shadowy valley with perspective is because of the lessons those kids imparted to us.

Establish some soul-feeding rituals in your life. Give some time, money, or encouragement to others in need. Pay it forward. What goes around comes around.

FIRE-STOKING HEAD TALK

IGNITE VISION.

Read and revisit your vision daily. If you don't have one, go back and read "Vision" again—it will take you through the process of creating one. This will spark energy inside of you. It will make you a magnet. You'll attract the resources you need to achieve each goal.

AFFIRM YOURSELF.

Words are not just a tool of communication, they're a tool of creation. They create an attitude of mind. They affect the emotions of the people around you. They're potent. Affirmations are the pep talk you have with yourself before the big game. Here are some of our favorites:

- I'm creative.
- I'm indestructible.
- I'm in demand.
- I get the job done.
- I do whatever it takes to achieve.
- No one will out-work me.
- I am the best follow-up person in the world.
- I eat challenges for breakfast.
- Obstacles create opportunity.
- I surround myself with good people.
- I look for the positive in any situation.
- I am blasting through the walls of my comfort zone.
- I got this. I can do this.

Speak your affirmations, but speak them like you mean them. Something will change inside of you if you make this a daily habit.

Best-selling author and documentarian Helie Lee describes it:

"I can! I will! I must!" This is an affirmation I taught to my children and their friends. When my children have a challenging task to accomplish, I tell them to speak that affirmation and to make their hands into fists and punch the air and scream, loud, "I can! I will! I must!" That creates energy and determination.

CREATE INTENTION.

Set the course of your day by asking yourself a couple questions:

How am I going to make a powerful difference in my life and the life of other people TODAY?

What can I do to move one step closer to my goals TODAY?

Answer these questions. Then suit up and tackle your daily action plan. Creating intention and taking action will silence the voices in your head that cast self-doubt and distract you from your goals.

CANCEL NEGATIVITY.

Listen to what you're silently speaking to yourself. Most of us say things to ourselves that we would never consider saying to a friend or even out loud to ourselves. Nothing will throw water on your passion like those silent accusations. It stokes negative internal energy that will show up like a neon sign in your body language.

When a negative thought springs up, nuke it. Reverse negative thoughts with a positive. Reframe them. "I am dreading this project," becomes, "I'm fired up to get this done and move on to the next thing."

Actress and author Mariel Hemingway describes negative thoughts:

Those voices of the past are not our voice. They are the voices of parents, teachers, peers. They can be like rude guests that come to dinner. They don't say please or thank you. They interrupt you. They complain about the meal you made. They tell you what a horrible host you are. If they were guests, you would kick them out. Too often we let these guests take up residence in our heads.

If those negative forces—demons, if you will—start taking control of you, there is no shame in seeking help. Invest in the therapy you need to reframe your thoughts and slay those demons.

FIRE-STOKING ALLIES

You can't choose your family, but you can choose your friends. Who are the top five people in your friend group? You'll become like the people you hang out with. They are your future. Choose your friends wisely. Find friends who keep you stoked.

If you spend time with passionate, determined, successful people, you're more likely to be passionate, determined, and successful. It's the mirror neuron thing, that part of our brains that stimulates us to emulate those around us (for good or evil). Make new friends who are accomplishing what you want to accomplish.

Many successful people freely share their success secrets. Seek out someone you want to emulate—a role model. You might not be able to meet them at the local hangout for a beer, but there are other ways to connect. Read their books, listen to their speeches, and attend their seminars.

Seminars are a great way to meet like-minded individuals. Even in a crowded room, it's likely that that audience is on a similar wavelength. Attend a seminar and make it your goal to cultivate a relationship with someone you meet.

Sometimes the most unlikely people can stoke your vehemence. Rosie was a waitress at a food truck that parked near Veterans Stadium. We would stop there early in the morning for a breakfast sandwich (usually fried bologna, egg, and cheese) and coffee.

Rosie would be there to greet us—hair teased and sprayed into a beehive, not a strand out of place. Her lips were ruby red; eyeliner, black and thick; eyeshadow, midnight blue. She looked ready for a night on the town—at the crack of dawn.

Rosie started our day with a jolt of confidence. She was a diehard Eagles fan and looked at us like we were her breakfast sandwiches. She treated us like heroes and made us feel like a million bucks. She was one of those fire-stoking people. Thank you, Rosie.

FIRE-STOKING JAM SESSIONS

Have you heard of Parkinson's law? Economist Cyril Parkinson coined it back in the 50s: *Work expands to fill the time available for completion.*[3] In other words, if you give yourself two years to prepare for a marathon or write a book, you'll take two years to do it.

If you want to turn up the heat on your productivity, cut the deadline in half. One of our mentors, JR Ridinger, put it this way: "Go Berserk for 90 days" and get it done. Kick into super human mode. You'll be amazed at what you're capable of. Don't worry about making a mess. You can clean it up later.

Put your family and associates on notice that you are putting the pedal to the metal for the next few weeks. Eliminate distractions. Dive in and make it happen.

Do what you can to raise your temperature that one degree Fahrenheit. It will raise your achievement from average to exceptional. It will be impossible to accept failure when you are vehemently set on accomplishing your vision.

Here is one caveat: don't overheat. When you overheat, you can do some real damage. Dennis shares a time when his vehemence got the best of him. We were in the locker room, getting ready for the game. The team put Dennis on a mission: take out Washington Redskins running back Benny Malone.

> *I was vehement. I was jacked up and mentally focused. Guess what? I took him out, alright. I knocked him out cold. Instead of feeling bad, I was stoked. I was high fiving and celebrating. Well, that little celebration cost me 10% of my salary. I was charged with promoting violence on the field.*

Don't confuse being vehement with being an idiot. Know where the on-off switch is. When you see that you're losing people because you're overzealous, it might be time to flip the switch.

VERACITY:

THE HABIT OF SPEAKING THE TRUTH

"Honesty is more than not lying. It is truth telling, truth speaking, truth living, and truth loving."

—James E. Faust

Your words are like your business card. They tell people who you are and what you have to offer them. The very first thing people want to know if they plan to do business with you is, "Can I trust you?" Veracity is the art of being straight up with people in a way that is effective—honest, but not cruel. It's building and maintaining trust. Here are some guidelines.

THINK BEFORE YOU SPEAK.

You choose what comes out of your mouth. You are in control of your tongue. Discipline that tongue to use language that is positive and productive, not negative and destructive. Think before you speak.

When you moan, whine, and complain, you become an energy bandit. You steal energy from yourself and the people who are listening to you. If you haven't figured this out yet, here's the truth: people don't want to listen to a downer.

On the other hand, when you speak with hope and optimism, you spark energy in yourself and the people listening to you. Winston Churchill, prime minister of the U.K. during WWII, is rumored to have said, "A pessimist sees the difficulty in every opportunity. An optimist sees the opportunity in every difficulty." If there ever was a reason to look on the dark side, watching your country get bombed to smithereens would be it. And yet he remained optimistic and determined to conquer the enemy and save the lives of his people.

Don't get us wrong: there are times to share challenges and air your grievances, but they should be with those who can provide worthwhile responses or a solution. If you complain to someone who can help with a situation, that's productive. When you complain to people who can't—or if you complain all the time about everything—that isn't. Controlling your tongue takes practice. Trust us, we know. Like many of you, we're still in training. But it pays off. When you have control of your tongue, you earn the respect and trust of the people around you.

BE BRAVE ENOUGH TO ASK FOR WHAT YOU WANT.

Whatever goals you set, you are going to have to get people to buy into them—your spouse, potential business partners, coaches, and mentors. If you don't communicate clearly, how are they going to know how to support you?

This is particularly important if you are in sales or any other profession that requires persuading others. Whether you're selling an idea, product, service, TV pilot, supplement, or seminar, you're going to have to ask for a yes or a no at the end of your pitch. Sometimes that's a tough thing to do. Discomfort with asking for the sale is often fear-driven. You fear appearing pushy. You fear failure or rejection. Just like we talked about in the "Valor" section, don't let it get the best of you.

Be straight up and let people know what you want. "No" can mean many things. It can mean the person you are pitching needs more information or clarification. It can mean "not now," and sometimes it can mean "not ever." That's okay too. Accept it and move on.

DON'T OVER-PROMISE.

As a general rule, under-promise and over-deliver. Don't be one of those frauds that will say anything to get what they want. You know the type:

we call them takers—those folks who will beg, borrow, and steal to get what they want, people that are always on the take.

Givers, on the other hand, seek to understand the needs of the person they're dealing with. Their goal is to give accurate information so the other person can make an intelligent, informed decision.

Dennis is one of the top earners in the network marketing industry. A key to his success is his commitment to speaking the truth.

> *Don't mislead someone into thinking that success is easier than it is. Be clear on what it takes. If you explain the process and it turns the candidate away from partnering with you, consider yourself lucky that you didn't waste your time. On the other hand, the prospect who gets it and says yes has a higher likelihood of success. In my experience, the prospect who walked away sometimes comes back because you spoke the truth. They trust your guidance.*

Ask yourself, "Can I back up what I am saying or selling?" Vince was a highly successful mortgage broker at one time.

> *I never made a promise that my underwriters could not back up. If I offered an outrageous deal, I got it done. We made a lot of people happy.*

DON'T EXPECT PEOPLE TO READ YOUR MIND.

They can't. If you want something done in a particular way or by a particular person, be clear in your instruction. If the person you are instructing is an employee, a client, or a teammate, make sure they understand what you're asking for. Have them repeat your instructions back to you. Simply ask, "Just to make sure we're all on the same page, what are the expectations?" If they didn't understand the first time, correct it. If they get it right, move forward.

SPEAK TRUTH RESPECTFULLY.

Research shows that there is a powerful radar in our head that is continually scanning the environment for threats.[4] If that radar perceives a threat through our speech and/or body language, it triggers the production of stress hormones—like cortisol, which we talked about earlier. These stress hormones can prime the listener to withdraw or to fight, so be careful how you respond to people. If your language (speech as well as body language) is demeaning and dismissive, you will turn that person off or cause them to attack.

On the other hand, sometimes the truth hurts, especially in competitive sports or the performing arts. If you are mentoring or coaching someone, you have to be willing to dish it out and you have to be willing to take it.

If you screw up on the pro football field, the painful reality is your mistake is captured on film. We hated it when we messed up. During film study, you sat there while the error is replayed over and over again in front of everyone: your teammates and your coaches. The mistake gets bigger with every replay. By the time the coach finishes critiquing the performance, you're ready to crawl under the table. You can't breathe. Your skin better be thick as an elephant's. If you're in the real world of competition, you're going to hear, and sometime give, criticism. It's part of living. If you can't handle the truth, get out of the game.

This applies to non-competitive coaching too, like life coaching and wellness coaching. One of the wellness coaches Dennis works with shared an incident where a diabetic woman was being evasive and combative about changing **her** way of eating. She was in danger of premature death if she did not get her diabetes under control. One day she called the coach from a donut shop. "I just want you to know I am done with your coaching. I'm going to eat a donut." The coach softly, but with authority, responded, "You're the boss, my friend. But at some point, you're going to have to choose between donuts and feet." She then startled the client by hanging up.

That client was miffed but soon got back on track. The outcome? Her diabetes is under control. She ditched the walker and wheelchair she was using to get around. She went from sitting in a lounge chair all day to doing water aerobics three times a week. She reduced the number of medications she was taking by 70%. Her supervising physician was thrilled. The client told the coach, "I was mad at first, but that conversation was my turning point. You saved my life."

Yes, sometimes speaking a hard truth can save a life—even your own.

RESPOND TO CRITICISM WITH AN OPENNESS TO LEARN.

Are you coachable? If not, you'll have a hard time reaching your full potential. When we take criticism personally, we miss the opportunity to gain insight into how our words and actions are affecting others.

We have seen athletes who consider themselves exceptional. They don't need anyone to tell them what to do. They think they have it all figured out. It's called a fixed mindset: if they are un-coachable, they're going to get cut.

Have a developing mindset. Always look for ways to improve your performance. Don't just be open to coaching, actively seek it out. Coaching from a competent mentor can help you reach the next level.

We were blessed to play for Coach Dick Vermeil—the man who turned three losing teams into winners. If you had the courage to ask his opinion on something you did, he would tell you exactly what he thought. Sometimes it hurt. He would say, "If you don't want to know what I'm thinking, don't ask." Coach was straight up because he cared. His correction was not rejection, it was direction.

WHEN YOU'RE WRONG, ADMIT IT.

It diffuses the situation. It shows maturity. It can inspire the other person to respond in kind, leading you closer to mutual understanding and a solution. Continuing to pretend that you were right all along will alienate the person you're talking to and make you look like an ass. Take the knee and learn. Admitting you're wrong doesn't mean you're stupid—it means that you're wise enough to admit your mistake.

BE A RESPONDER, NOT A REACTOR.

When someone says something that makes you mad, instead of reacting impulsively, take a deep breath, relax, and listen. This especially applies to your relationships with business partners, friends, and family. Make an effort to understand what they're trying to say. Ask questions. The twenty-four hour rule applies. Hold your tongue for a day, then speak. This helps to avoid damaging a relationship. Communication is irrevocable; you can't unsay anything, so be sure you don't say things you don't mean.

AVOID UNPRODUCTIVE TRASH TALK.

There are times to candidly discuss ugly realities with a trusted friend or counselor—that's not what we mean. We mean gossip (malicious talk) and judgment (malicious opinions). However you label it, most trash talk serves no good purpose other than to make you and the people you're talking to feel better, but that relief very seldom lasts.

There are some exceptions. In football, there's a lot of trash talking. On the field, it can be used as a strategic distraction so one can gain a competitive edge. Vince puts it this way:

> Trash talk never bothered me. I loved it when I got under the skin of a defensive back. They hated it when they got blocked downfield (we could block below the waist then). I did it often and with passion (a.k.a. vehemence). They would then trash talk me, and it made me laugh. When they started whining, I knew I had them. I was in their heads.

There was also a lot of friendly locker room trash talk. We used it to encourage camaraderie and diffuse tension, but sometimes it went south. Trash talk aimed at discrediting or embarrassing someone was not okay. Trash talk that escalated to the point of physical harm, like road rage, was most definitely not okay.

A good way to judge if trash talk is serving a useful purpose is to evaluate the outcome. Did it strengthen team unity or damage it? Did it make someone stronger or did it tear them down?

DON'T OVERLOAD YOUR MOUTH WITH YOUR ASS.

We came out on the wrong end a few times for sure, but Dennis gets the floor on this one.

I was a rookie at the time, and Bill Bergey was the All-Pro middle linebacker. During practice, we faced off at the line of scrimmage daily. Bergey taught me many lessons, including this one.

After practice one day, a sports writer from the Philadelphia Journal *asked me, "Dennis, what do you want to accomplish this season?" On reflection, I should have said something like, "I look forward to making the Philadelphia Eagles squad and contributing to building a championship team." No, not me. I said, "I want to knock Bill Bergey on his ass!" Keep in mind, Bergey was one of the best linebackers not only on the Eagles, but in the entire NFL. Bergey was the shiznit. Admittedly, I was a bit cocky. Hey, I figured If I could take down Bergey, I would qualify to play against anybody.*

Surprise, surprise. The next day, on the sports page of the *Philadelphia Journal*, the headline was "Rookie Center Wants to Knock Bill Bergey on His Ass."

Did I really say that? I knew this was not going to be a good day. During practice, field offense against defense, Bergey didn't say much, but things turned intense during the thud drill. During this drill, you're supposed to take a couple steps full speed, then back off on the hit. Not on this play: I came off the thud drill tempo and Bill came full speed and almost took my head off.

Okay, I deserved that. But on the next play, I was ready for combat. The veins in my neck were popping out. I had my weight forward. I was going to hit that guy as hard as I could. The quarterback called the signal, I snapped the ball, and with a driving first step, I thrust my weight into Bergey. It didn't go as planned. He played me like a matador. I flew past him and landed face-down in the dirt. He came over to me after that tough day and said, "Rookie, don't overload you mouth with your ass." Lesson learned.

Make no mistake. With every last laugh, veracity—framing the truth (with discretion)—plays a role. It's a non-negotiable part of your success journey.

VITALITY:

THE LIFE FORCE OR ABILITY TO LIVE

*"Health is not merely the absence of disease;
it is the balance of mind, body and soul."*

—Hippocrates

Michael Jordan playing basketball, Joaquin Cortes dancing, or Mick Jagger singing—we love to watch gifted people get down. We are in awe of that explosive combination of physical energy and mental focus— vitality in action.

Whether performing at the office or on stage, on the playground with your kids, or in the bedroom with your lover, vitality drives performance. We all need it. Just like a fire, vitality must be stoked. It's energy. And just like a fire, if you don't stoke it, it dies. We stoke it with the foods we eat and the lives we live.

Though there are different diet and lifestyle needs (depending on age, gender, and level of activity), the basics for living well are the same for all of us. Let's talk about them. Then we will share the specifics on how we have kept our vitality alive through the years.

FOOD

Every top athlete knows about the training table. The training table offers meals designed to fuel the body with energy and repair/build muscle mass. The athlete who doesn't "come to the table" is pretty easy to spot. It's the guy with the jelly belly or the one missing the clutch at a critical moment.

To boil it down, this is what the training table teaches:

- You can't put on muscle without eating protein.
- You'll feel hungry all the time if you don't eat healthy fat.
- You need carbs like broccoli and berries to stoke your mojo.
- You're going to get fat and lazy if you're inhaling sleeves of Oreo cookies every day.

Back in the day, our training table was not very sophisticated. The go-to meal was the beloved hoagie. They would be waiting for us in the locker room after practice. That's right—a real, two-fisted Philly hoagie! Sliced lunch meat, cheese, lettuce, tomatoes, and sliced raw onions jammed into a foot-long Philly roll soaked in olive oil. All the food groups included: carbs, proteins, and fats—and plenty of them. Artery cloggers. Not a good idea for the long haul, but it gave us the energy we needed to get through those long days on the training field.

Times have changed. The training table is now more in line with the principles expressed by *In Defense of Food* by Michael Pollan: "Eat real food. Not too much. Mostly plants." And don't forget the lean protein. That's a sensible training table for all of us.

WATER

Our brains are mostly made of fat and water. A bit humbling, isn't it? Water is essential for the brain to function. If the levels drop by even 1%, you can experience short-term dementia—memory loss, trouble focusing, and feeling tired and dazed.[5] The brain does not store water. That's why it's important to sip on water throughout the day, every day.

It cracks us up to think that it was once taboo to drink water while exercising because it would cause cramps. It's just the opposite—hydrate, hydrate, hydrate! In fact, the American College of Sports Medicine recommends you drink 16–20 ounces of water 3–4 hours before your workout and 8–12 ounces 10–14 minutes before your workout in addition to your normal water intake.[6] When muscles don't have water, they don't work efficiently. You're more prone to cramps and you're more likely to be sore as hell the next day.

Water can clear sodium, urea (a compound that results from the breakdown of proteins), and toxins from the body. This decreases the likelihood of kidney-related problems and helps with bowel regularity. Your body cannot eliminate properly if you don't have enough water.

A good rule of thumb is to drink at least 64 ounces of water a day—more if you're exercising, under stress, trying to lose weight, or drinking coffee or alcohol.

For some, the thirst signal is clear. For many, this signal is not strong, especially as we age. Some just don't have that urge to drink. If you have trouble drinking enough water, track your intake for a while. It will help you develop the habit of hydrating. There are free phone apps to help you stay on track, too. Or just go old school: mark your daily water intake on the back of your business card or a piece of paper in your pocket. Track daily until it's a habit.

SUPPLEMENTS

Unless you're living in the Garden of Eden, you might need to take supplements. Even if we try to eat right, chemical fertilizers, stress, pollutants, and medications create gaps that must be filled.

If you use supplements, beware: not all supplements are created equal. Choose products from a reputable source—companies dedicated to clinical evidence who offer quality ingredients at the right dosage. Make sure the supplements are manufactured in an FDA-approved facility implementing GMP (Good Manufacturing Practices) standards.

Even a supplement with the best raw ingredients is useless if the body cannot absorb it. Some nurses call those supplements that go from mouth to south bedpan bullets—they go out the same way they come in. Find a supplement that the body can absorb.

If you have trouble with pills or are concerned about absorption, consider an isotonic solution—a liquid that has the same pH and same fluid density as your tears and blood. When taken on an empty stomach, it's up to 95% bioavailable within a few minutes, significantly increasing the chances of delivering the nutritional payload you need.

So how do we know what nutrients we're missing? That depends on a lot of factors: health goals, diet, lifestyle, and level of pollutants in your water and air.

Here are some basics that, according to studies, have been shown to support the average person's health goals. We're not doctors, so make sure you consult your physician or a health professional before making any major diet or lifestyle changes.

- **A Multivitamin and Mineral Formula:** A high-quality multivitamin fills the gaps in your diet. Find one that provides all the essential vitamins and minerals you need to take in daily. (Not sure what these are? Check out the guidelines from the T. H. Chan School of Public Health at Harvard.[7]) Make sure they are offered at optimal concentrations.

- **Fish Oil:** According to the American Heart Association, research has shown that omega-3 fatty acids support healthy triglyceride levels, the reduction of atherosclerotic plaque (the stuff that clogs your arteries and can lead to heart attacks), and healthy blood pressure.[8] You can get your omegas from wild-caught, cold-water fish (such as salmon or mackerel—light fish like cod or flounder tend to have less fat and thus fewer omega-3s), or you can supplement with fish oil. Again, be careful: many fish oils on the market are not offered at the proper concentration. Look for 3:2 ration of EPA (eicosapentaenoic acid) to DHA (docosahexaenoic acid), and aim to get a combined total of 3,000 mg of omega-3s daily. Some fish oil supplements have traces of toxins, like mercury and dioxin (common in the fish from which they're extracted). Be sure to choose an oil that has been quantified for purity.

- **B-Complex:** The Bs are essential to creating the fuel you need to sustain your energy levels. They can easily be depleted by stress, caffeine, excess sugar, and some medications. Be sure to get the activated forms of vitamin B (e.g. 5-methyltetrahydrofolic)—because they don't have to go through a conversion process, these are easier for your body to metabolize.

- **Antioxidants:** As the name implies, antioxidants counteract oxidation. Oxidation is to the cells in our body what rust is to metal. Antioxidants are believed to play a role in preventing the development of chronic diseases like cancer, heart disease, Alzheimer's, rheumatoid arthritis, and cataracts. There are many types of antioxidants and they vary depending on the source. You can find them in herbs, spices, fruits and vegetables, black tea, turmeric, blueberries, grapes, citrus fruits, and greens.

▫ **Vitamin D:** Deficiencies of this vitamin are associated with premature aging, cancer, osteoporosis, and arthritis. As we age, our ability to convert vitamin D from what we eat or from exposure to sunlight into a usable form decreases. It makes sense to supplement to make sure you are getting an adequate amount. Research suggests that Vitamin K2 can help make the most of your vitamin D supplements.[9] Vitamin K2 helps get the calcium into your bones instead of having it lodging in undesirable sites, like your arteries.

Curious about what we use? Check out Recommended Resources for a list of products we recommend.

SLEEP

Stop trying to burn the candle at both ends! It's not only a waste of a good candle; it pretty much guarantees you will not perform your best in any area of life. Though it varies from person to person, most need around eight hours of sleep a night to stay healthy.

While you enjoy your rest, your body is hard at work. A burly crew of hormones rebuild and reset your body. These hormones erase fine lines on your face. They build bone and muscle, heal tissue, process and organize your thoughts, and let you wake up energized. If you go long enough without a good night's sleep, your health will break down. There are no exceptions.

Here are some healthy sleep tips from the experts at the Sleep Disorders Institute:

▫ Exercise every day. Even twenty minutes of walking can help keep stress hormones from interfering with your sleep.

- Avoid large meals just before bedtime. An active digestive system can disrupt sleep.

- Avoid caffeine, nicotine, and other stimulants within four hours of bedtime.

- Avoid before-bed snacks, particularly grains and sugars. This will raise blood sugar and inhibit sleep. Later, when blood sugar drops too low (hypoglycemia), you might wake up and not be able to fall back asleep.

- Minimize noise and temperature extremes; your bedroom should be comfortably cool, about 68 degrees.

- Don't read, watch television, or work in bed. Use the bed only to sleep (and, you know, for sex).

- Some people find the sound of white noise or nature sounds soothing. Using a noise machine or an app may help you relax.

- Sleep in complete darkness or as close to it as possible. Even the tiniest bit of light in a room can disrupt your circadian rhythm and your pineal gland's ability to produce melatonin and serotonin, two naturally-occurring hormones that help you sleep.

- Wear socks to bed. Your feet often feel cold before the rest of the body. Keeping them warm can reduce the likelihood of waking mid-cycle.

- Get the vitamins, minerals, amino acids, and enzymes that support a good night's sleep. Here are a few you might consider:

    - **B VITAMINS** like Vitamin B6 can help prevent insomnia. Pantothenic acid (B5) helps manage stress.

    - **CALCIUM/MAGNESIUM** has a sedative effect on the body. A deficiency causes restlessness and wakefulness.

    - **CHROMIUM** is often effective for someone with a blood sugar problem that is keeping them awake at nights.

    - **L-TRYPTOPHAN** is an essential amino acid that converts to serotonin, a natural, sleep-inducing chemical. It also enhances the brain's ability to produce melatonin, the hormone that regulates your body's natural inner clock.

- **MELATONIN** is a hormone secreted naturally by the pineal gland. In several studies, taking melatonin (5 mg or higher) has proven helpful in inducing and maintaining sleep.

Remember: if minor adjustments do not relieve your sleep issues, it's a good idea to seek the counsel of a health professional. A cumulative sleep deficit—whether from stress, lifestyle, or a sleep disorder—can result in serious health consequences.

One last thing on the sleep stuff, especially for those of you who work from home. There is no guilt in taking a little n—excuse us, "power napping." It takes the edge off afternoon sleepiness if kept under thirty minutes. Try napping for twenty minutes a day and see how you feel.

EXERCISE

Did you know that sitting might be as bad for your health as smoking? It is estimated that Americans now sit more than half of their waking hours.[10]

One study claims that if you're over twenty-five, every hour you spend sitting is as lethal as smoking one cigarette. That means four hours of sitting—like many of us do at the office or at home after a long day of work—is like inhaling four cigarettes.

Though that fact might be debatable, this fact is not: the human body was designed for movement, not sitting in a chair or lounging on the couch for hours at a time. Prolonged sitting stops the production of vital enzymes and hormones needed to metabolize fat and keep blood sugar stable. It also does a number on your body, leaving you with muscle aches and stiffness. Standing desks have seen a surge in popularity in response to these studies. Standing not only helps you feel better, but it can stimulate creative thinking, too. (Now that's what we call "thinking on your feet!")

To maintain your health, Dr. Michael Roizen of the Cleveland Clinic recommends standing up and taking a quick, 1- to 3-minute break to stretch or walk every half hour or so throughout the day.

It doesn't require fancy equipment or much thought to move more during your day. Here are a few ideas:

- Skip the drive-through at the bank. Park and go inside.
- Replace your office chair with a therapy ball.
- Invest in a standing desk.
- Go to the playground with your kids and play!
- Walk while you talk on the phone.
- Instead of meeting a friend for cup of coffee, meet for a hike or a mall walk.
- Instead of sitting and reading a book, listen to an audiobook while walking.
- Get a reliable pedometer. Calculate how many steps you walk a day, then increase 500 a day until you're walking 5,000–10,000 steps a day.
- Join a sport. We were active kids—thank God our parents introduced us to sports at an early age. Sports make movement fun. Golfing, cycling, running, team sports. Get active and have a blast.

Move consistently throughout the day, but also remember to spend at least thirty minutes breaking a sweat. Another favorite Dick Vermeil quote: "Nobody ever drowned in sweat!"

We know, we know—this is two gnarly guys talking. But breaking a sweat and building your body is for women, too. Here's what Janet Papale, former world-class gymnast, nationally renowned gymnastics coach, and Vince's wife, has to say about it.

Women shouldn't be afraid of muscle. You should love muscle. Muscle defies gravity as you age. When you sweat and work your body, everything is better. Your health is better, your sex is better, your self-esteem is better. You feel better about who you are and how you look. Don't be afraid to work out and work out hard. In one word: SWEAT!

STRESS MANAGEMENT

Yes, at times our lives get stressful, but probably not as stressful as the life of a Navy SEAL. We all must occasionally dodge a figurative bullet from time to time, but Navy SEALs face the possibility of confronting the real thing every day. Stress undermines our mental focus and our ability to intelligently respond to crisis. This is something a SEAL cannot afford. Guess what? Neither can you.

One way you can help clean up the stress mess? Breathe like a Navy SEAL. When you breathe deeply, oxygen pours into every cell of your body, improving mental concentration and physical stamina. The infusion of oxygen helps your body absorb vitamins and nutrients more efficiently. It creates more white blood cells to help with healing and maintaining a healthy immune system. Your muscles relax. Your blood pressure falls. Endorphins—the feel-good hormones—are released.

The SEALs have a technique for controlling stress with breath called 4x4 or box breathing. It's simple and effective.

1. Find a comfortable chair or place to lie down.
2. Inhale for four seconds.
3. Hold air in your lungs for four seconds.
4. Exhale for four seconds, emptying all the air in your lungs.
5. Hold your lungs empty for four seconds.
6. Repeat for as long as necessary until you feel refocused and relaxed.

GET A CHECKUP

Lack of energy can be an indicator of more serious problems. If you're chronically fatigued—constantly exhausted or frequently overcome by unexpected bouts of exhaustion regardless of the amount you sleep or rest—you need to see a knowledgeable health professional to determine if there are any problems that need to be addressed.

Now let's get personal. Here's how we stay fit.

DENNIS FRANKS'S VITALITY PLAN

I played center in college and in the NFL. My job was to set the tempo of every game. I was like a stick of dynamite burning down to the explosion that sets everything in motion. Mental focus, as well as physical energy, were critical to the success of each play.

In business, vitality is just as important. I do everything I can to keep my energy stoked. My colleagues call me Mr. Energy. I travel internationally, establishing brands and training those in my field how to market products and services. Recently, I traveled to seven countries on three continents and through four major time changes in seven weeks. That is a pace that even a young man would find difficult to sustain.

Staying fit is the key, but I have to work at it. I inherited the hard work, strength, and stamina genes from my steel-working father, Don, and my pro figure skater mother, Inge. But I also inherited the obesity gene (yes, I rocked 298 lbs. in the past). Those fat genes are always calling my name. There are plenty of days I wouldn't mind hanging out on the couch, inhaling snacks, and guzzling beer as I surf the sports channel.

Thank God research shows that environment trumps genes when it comes to achieving a healthy body index. I have cultivated habits that keep my weight in check and my vitality stoked.

But life is not all work: I golf and enjoy hiking in the Blue Ridge Mountains. My wife, Nancy, and I hang out with good friends as often as we can.

Regarding stress management, playing music helps me stay sane. I played music professionally after football as both a guitarist and a singer. I even enjoyed a stint rapping with the Philadelphia Eagles cheerleaders, the Liberty Bells. A well-regarded music producer asked me to record a Philadelphia Eagles fight rap song—"Eagles Battle Cry." We performed it at the 1980 NFC Championship game. I've played music in honkytonk bars and in coliseums filled with 20,000 people. I loved every minute of being on stage with a guitar and mic. (A warm shout-out to my fellow musicians in The Sky Travelers, Second Look, and the Honey James Band!)

Lately, my most devoted audience is my granddaughter, Izzy. That's great for now, but I have plans to reignite my music career. It's on my twenty-year vision statement. I have a lot of things planned between now and my 84th birthday. Sustaining my vitality is critical to achieving my goals.

DIET: Low glycemic impact food combinations (limited sugar and empty calorie intake), clean proteins, and essential fats. I work from a predetermined list of power foods instead of following a strict meal-by-meal diet.

SUPPLEMENTS: Multivitamin, omega-3s, curcumin, B complex, calcium, magnesium, vitamin D3, OPCs (antioxidants from grape seed, red wine extract, and French maritime pine bark), and astaxanthin.

SLEEP SCHEDULE: Bed by 11 p.m., up at 7 a.m. I used to kid myself that I could survive on five hours of sleep. I discovered the hard way that that's not the case. Seven to eight hours a night is my minimum.

STRESS MANAGEMENT: Golf, music, and hiking.

FITNESS TRAINING: I'm a big believer in investing in the people who can get you on track and keep you there. Choose the best. My personal trainer is Jason Davis. He's not only a certified personal trainer and strength and conditioning coach, he's also a certified nutrition counselor, natural bodybuilding and figure coach, and a certified health and lifestyle coach. Our workouts focus on three key areas: strength, endurance, and stability. We include strength exercises and cardio in every workout and alternate our secondary focus on endurance and stability during the week. Check out Recommended Resources for a sample workout.

VINCE PAPALE'S VITALITY PLAN

Apart from the inevitable injuries that come when your throw your body around a football field, I had always been remarkably healthy. That changed when, at fifty-five, I went in for a colorectal cancer screening. I felt perfectly fine. I wouldn't have gone if my wife didn't insist on it. Quite frankly, I was shocked when they found a polyp in my lower intestine—a big one, and it was cancerous. Not good news.

Fortunately, we caught it before the cancer had spread to my liver. That made me a believer in routine cancer colon screenings (Yes, that means even those of you who feel amazingly fit. If you're over fifty, you should be going once a year). I was and still am really fit, but you better believe I have those screenings on my calendar. As a matter of fact, I recently had a screening. After sixteen years of living cancer-free, my colon is green and clean. If it weren't for a routine colonoscopy in June 2001, I wouldn't be here to share my victories with you. I guess you could call this one of my last laughs, eh?

A key to my success in football was being one of the fittest guys on the field. I didn't stop training even when the season was over. There was nothing that Coach Vermeil threw at me that I couldn't handle. At thirty, I felt I could will my body to do anything that I could envision— your basic mind-over-matter syndrome.

It was a different era then. We ate steak, eggs, and hoagies all the time. Supplements, yoga, and all those new wellness ideas that you find in locker rooms today—are you kidding? Not back then. Sports medicine wasn't even part of our vocabulary. The thought of having a nutritionist on staff would have been considered "a little out there." I think that's why a lot of older guys from that era struggle just to walk to the mailbox.

After seven decades on this planet, I'm one of those fruit and veggie guys. Yes, after colon cancer, my diet changed. I continue to work out to maintain my physical strength and stamina, but now I put a big emphasis on my core (a.k.a. my gut). I've adjusted my workout regimen to include a lot more stretching.

Hey, you're only as pretty as you feel. Right now, I'm feeling pretty: not ready to compete in a decathlon or play in the NFL, but good enough for the demands and expectations that I have for myself—which are very high!

DIET: Cut out anything white—white flour, white sugar, white bread, white potatoes, and white rice. They're empty carbs. I substituted wheat bread for white bread at first, but I've since learned that many kinds of wheat bread are genetically altered. I've switched to sprouted grain bread. If the boys from the Glenolden project could see me now!

Cook at home as often as possible. You will have more control over what you eat and save a ton of money in the process.

Eat more whole food—fruits, vegetables, seeds, nuts. Eat them without added sugar, salt, and preservatives. Trust me, your taste buds will adjust just like mine reluctantly did.

SUPPLEMENTS: Multivitamins, omega-3s, and OPC-3s.

SLEEP SCHEDULE: Bed by 10 or 11 p.m., up at 6 a.m.

STRESS MANAGEMENT: I love working in my yard. I do my best creative thinking while doing yard work. I lather up a good sweat and admire the fruits of my labor. During summer, when I was in college at St. Joe's, I worked with my Uncle Dom, a landscape architect. I pulled a rake eight to ten hours a day. I had an incredibly strong back and shoulders. This helped me as a pole vaulter in my younger days. I can still pull a mean rake.

I enjoy riding my beach bike around the neighborhood and walking our rescue dog, Bandit.

To wind down, give me a good action novel and I'm in heaven. Janet and I usually end the day by reading our books. She likes to devour self-help books—I'm hopeless, so it's all action for me.

Oh, yeah—the best stress reliever? Hanging with my family, anytime, anywhere, and any way.

FITNESS PLAN: Without a doubt, exercise eliminates stress, fatigue, and anxiety. It also can help you recover from major surgery (such as a bowel excision or resection). Here are my basics—the same as they were forty years ago when I launched a circuit training program for myself and the athletes I coached. I'm an old school fundamentals kind of guy who still defines a good workout by how much I sweat!

Oh yeah, one more thing: put that darned mobile device away. That's probably half the reason for your stress. Exercise is your time. It's all about you. Think about the good things; do creative thinking; visualize yourself living out your fantasy. Then get to work. Remember, "Nobody ever drowned in sweat!"

WORKOUT REGIMEN: My exercise routine focuses on endurance, toning, strength, weight management, and staying dead sexy! I do strength and endurance training three or four times a week, about fifty minutes per session. On off days, I do some form of cardio. I ride a bike or simply walk briskly for an hour. Other cardio options are walking/jogging on a treadmill, plyometrics, skipping rope, using a rowing machine, jogging in place, or using an elliptical, stepper, ropes, etc.

My trainer recommends that you exercise within 55 to 85 percent of your MHR (maximum heart rate) for at least 20 to 30 minutes to get the best results from aerobic exercise. The MHR (roughly calculated as 220 minus your age) is the upper limit of what your cardiovascular system can handle during physical activity. Every workout, I try to do twenty minutes of cardio at my target heart rate.

One of the most undervalued part of any workout is the pre and post: stretch, stretch, stretch! Stretching prepares your muscles for work and helps them recover with the buildup and relief of lactic acid—the stuff your muscles "burn" to move. Stretching keeps you from getting hurt and makes exercising on back-to-back days easier—don't forget to do it!

My program is nowhere near what it was when I was playing. Heck, this would have been my warm-up. But after two new knees, two busted shoulders, and two blown up feet from my track days, my sample program works great for me and will no doubt help you. You'll find it in Recommended Resources.

VIGOR:

THE ABILITY TO
THRIVE AND SURVIVE

*"Energy is contagious, positive and negative alike.
I will forever be mindful of what and who
I am allowing in my space."*

—Alex Elle

Vitality is the physical energy you need to fulfill your vision. Vigor is the steady flow of emotional energy through mind, body, and spirit. You need to maintain your vigor to stay the course. That means getting rid of the things that drain it—the vigor vampires in your life. These are people, dynamics, and habits that prey on your energy. If you don't eliminate them, you'll have a hard time reaching your full potential. Here is a list of some of those vigor vampires to avoid.

TOXIC FRIENDSHIPS

They come in all shapes and sizes with a common goal of getting you off track. It's like a bucket of crabs: one crab attempts to escape, and the others clamber up its ass trying to pull it back into the bucket. Like James Taylors's lyric in "You've Got a Friend," "They'll hurt you and desert you. They'll take your soul if you let them...but don't you let them."

Here is a list of hurters and deserters:

- **The Funny Guy** with his well-aimed, rude put-downs.

- **The Well-Meaning Friend** who tries to distract you from your goals.

- **The Downer** who constantly gives you the reasons your efforts won't work.

- **The Ball-Dropper** who doesn't keep his end of the bargain.

- **The Whiner** who drives you crazy with their complaints.

- **The Know-It-All** who doesn't lift a finger but knows what YOU need to do.

- **The Friendly Underminer** who greets you with a smile and destroys you behind your back.

Lose 'em. They'll disrupt the rhythm of your life and make you doubt yourself.

Ken Mok, the producer of *America's Next Top Model*, describes a friendship he had to lose:

> As I was moving up in the business, I had a friend. He was my best friend. We had been friends since the seventh grade, but he became toxic. He worked in the business but was not achieving the success that I was. As I was moving ahead, he continually tried to undermine me. I realized very clearly what his motivation was. He was jealous. After a while, I had to ask myself, "What is this person doing? Why is he doing this? What is his motivation?" Even though this guy had been my friend since I was thirteen years old, I had to cut off the friendship. He was a drain on my energies and my psyche.

When you can't lose 'em, ignore 'em. There are people that you can't entirely remove from your life—parents, children, spouses, or people above you on the corporate ladder. Though you might have to spend time with them, spend as little as possible. You are not doing them or yourself a favor by allowing their negativity to drain your vigor.

Vince found himself in the bucket of crabs several times:

When word got out that I was giving that free agent thing a shot, all sorts of crabs crawled up my back. "You can't do it, man. You're too old. It's never been done before. Geez, you didn't even play college football, dude!" Even Dennis (I gotta needle you on this one, bud), who is now my "brothuh from another mothuh," razed me. "You're too pretty, man. Pro ball is going to mess up that face."

Some of these were people I competed against in tryouts. They were my prospective teammates. I had no alternative but to hang with them, so I went into selective hearing mode. I tuned out those who were tearing me down and listened to my soul. I was going to get this done. Through it all, I found out who my true friends were. Yes, Dennis became one of the truest. When I was on the field getting bullied, he was the one who had my back, who encouraged me to press on.

Tell it like it is. Let the crabs know you're serious about your goal. If they're discouraging you from reaching your objectives or undermining your efforts in word or deed, you will need to spend less time together.

Spend time with your true friends, the ones who are in your court cheering you on as you roll toward your goals.

DYSFUNCTIONAL PARTNERSHIPS

Strategic alliances change. Someone who might have been a partner in one endeavor might not be the best partner for another. There's nothing wrong with that. It doesn't mean the friendship must end, it may just mean the working relationship needs to change. Each goal requires the right people to make it work. Attempting a venture with the wrong people will steal your vigor.

Dysfunctional partnerships happen all the time. Every NFL team begins the season with the goal of qualifying for a championship—conference, division, or Super Bowl. It takes a fifty-three-man roster to make it happen. Head coaches will not hesitate to eliminate someone who is not rowing in the same direction as the team. That person might be talented and fun to be around, but it doesn't matter. When it comes to the team, no one person is greater than the whole.

Dennis was a member of several different bands throughout his music career. Bands, like families, can become dysfunctional. You can leave a band or replace the member who is bringing negative mojo. And you should. Members of any team need to have a common vision and energy. That is the only way you will ever achieve success.

DISTRACTIONS

Success only becomes a reality for those who stay focused. The definition of focus?

Follow
One
Course
Until
Successful

This can be a challenge for entrepreneurial types. Entrepreneurs are, by nature, idea generators. They see opportunities at every turn. This is not a bad thing, but it needs to be tempered. It can easily get you off track.

Sometimes it's hard to discern between a great opportunity and a distraction. It is especially hard when you decide to pursue what looks like a great opportunity and you hit a snag.

Dennis was invited to play guitar and sing with country artist Stacy Whited. She was recording her album, *GIVE*, and asked him to join her on a song called "All the Way." One of his goals was to develop as a musician, and this opportunity seemed in line with that goal. He was jazzed. He met Stacy and her husband, David, at a Nashville recording studio.

Come to find out, they wanted me to play guitar and sing harmony. The guitar part was no problem, but sing harmony? Wow. I was a melody singer. I'm self-taught. I started out as a garage band musician and worked my way through the ranks.

Shifting gears was tougher then he thought. He made several attempts to harmonize but was not nailing it. Time is money when you're renting a Nashville studio.

Should I pack up and go home? Was this a mistake? Should I cut my (and their) losses and bail? I decided no! This opportunity was totally in line with my vision. I called an audible. We requested an ear piece and let another musician sing harmony in my ear. It worked. I could follow. I'm glad I did not give in to the temptation to quit. That is a project I am proud to have been part of.

A simple solution to make you distraction-proof:

- Revisit, read, and meditate on your goal statements and your vision board. On days you are particularly distracted or discouraged, read it several times. Recommit yourself to its fulfillment daily.
- Life moves fast. Opportunities may hit you in the face when you least expect them. When presented with an opportunity, ask yourself, "Does this line up with my vision?" If so, seize it! Make adjustments (call an audible) as needed, like Dennis and the ear plug.
- If the opportunity doesn't line up, let it pass. It's a distraction from the next great step.

PROCRASTINATION

Putting off doing something that needs doing happens occasionally to all of us. The problem is when it becomes a pattern. Chronic procrastination erodes your vigor. It's self-imposed sabotage and never ends well; down the road there will be anxiety and regret.

One strategy for overcoming this life-squandering habit is to learn how to manage your time. A basic tool of time management is the to-do list. Master it, and you will increase your productivity dramatically. You just need a notebook and pen. If you are the techy type, there are plenty of to-do apps. Whichever writing tools you choose, follow these steps:

- **Before you go to bed, make the next day's to-do list.** Include on it everything that comes to mind that you need to get done.
- **Make subcategories to help you prioritize.**
  - **Do Now:** These are the most pressing tasks that need to be completed the next day. Make time for them in your schedule. Be sure to consider your energy levels when you schedule them. Mentally or emotionally challenging activities should be scheduled when energy is high: if you are a morning person, get the tough stuff done first thing in the morning; night owls, put it after dinner. The less-energetic or mindless activities can be done when energy is lower. Scheduling difficult or involved tasks when you aren't at peak motivation may mean a task goes unfinished.
  - **Do Later:** These are less-pressing tasks that are going to be scheduled for a later time—a different day, week, or month. Make sure you schedule them in a reasonable amount of time—not too close or too far out. This is called "strategic procrastination."
  - **Delegate:** These are tasks you can give to someone else to complete. If you don't learn to delegate, especially in business, you're going to be running a race with a monkey on your back. Those monkeys will harass your mind and get you off track. Don't feed them. Find qualified and reliable support people. Delegate the task and trust them to do it. Consider hiring a virtual assistant to do your social media management. Hire someone to clean your house. Use a mail-order meal service during crunch times.

Once you get your to-do system in place, it should only take about fifteen minutes a day to update. You will be amazed at the difference this habit will make in your life. It will decrease the night-time anxiety you feel because life seems so out of control, enhance your mental focus and attitude, and help you design the life you were intended to live.

If this isn't the best system for you, find one that works for you. Ultra-successful serial entrepreneur Cosmo DeNicola has a different strategy:

I am super organized. It's one of my biggest assets. Like right now, I'm staring at three bins. Keep in mind, I own several technology companies so I have access to all sorts of tools to keep me organized, but I use bins. I have bins labeled "Today," "Tomorrow," and "Later." On the wall of my office, I have nine separate whiteboards. Each board reflects a different company and contains the small goals that must be achieved. When those goals are achieved, they are erased.

MONEY ANXIETY

Money is a common source of stress that can steal your vigor in a big way. Those with serious money problems—those with more stress—have a higher likelihood of headaches, depression, heart attacks, muscle pain, and digestive problems.[11]

There are a few things you need to learn if you are going to solve your money woes.

- You should have a handle on how much money is coming in and how much is going out. This will help you put together a reasonable budget.

- You need to learn the difference between a need and a want. A need is something you must have to survive (e.g., food and shelter); a want is something you would like to have NOW (e.g., a mansion in a gated community)! There's nothing wrong with wanting things. Your vision statement is full of things you want. The important thing is to not jump the gun before you have the resources. That can lead to vigor-sucking anxiety.

- You also need to know the difference between a debt and an investment. Debt means you borrow money to be paid back with interest. In other words, you're paying for your money. Be careful with debt. It can enslave you. It can limit your choices. It can force you to work at a job that you hate just because you must pay the bills. An investment means leveraging your money to create more prosperity in your life. It's not just buying stock or putting money into a cause or company: a well-chosen training experience or seminar is an investment, too. It's an opportunity to learn new skills and may help save you time and money down the road. Don't shortchange yourself by not getting the training you need to succeed.

If you don't know how to construct a budget or get out of debt, work with a financial planner or a credit counselor. Make sure that anybody that gives you advice about your money is a fiduciary—that requires them, by law, to only give you advice that will benefit YOU, not advice that benefits them.

ALL WORK, NO PLAY

This is the ultimate vigor vampire. You need joy in the journey if you're going to sustain vigor. Make time to celebrate your successes.

When we were playing for the Eagles, we lost plenty of games, but we would celebrate the small wins: a great tackle, a well-executed strategy, a well-called audible. Hey, sometimes just getting through a practice during scorching temperatures and suffocating humidity was worth a celebration.

Living a celebratory life has a biochemical effect. Setting aside time to acknowledge your success gets your happy neurotransmitters, dopamine and serotonin, pulsing. These hormones are the very same substances that get people hooked on gambling, nicotine, and alcohol. Why not cultivate a healthy addiction to achievement?

The "Last Laugh" photo captures a moment of celebration. Big, life-changing achievements (like being on the team that broke the Eagles' losing streak) are the result of daily, small wins. So celebrate your little victories. And don't forget to thank the people who helped you achieve them.

VICTORY:

THE ACCOMPLISHMENT OF AN AIM OR PURPOSE

"The ultimate victory in competition is derived from the inner satisfaction of knowing that you have done your best and that you have gotten the most out of what you had to give."

—Howard Cosell

You ran the race and broke the tape.

You built that successful business.

You lost the weight.

You sold product to your first customer.

You beat the odds.

You made the team.

You earned the Who's Nuts? t-shirt.

Fist pumps and end zone dances are in order. Reward yourself with a cold beer, a nice vacation, a new dress, or a new car—whatever befits the occasion. Don't forget to thank the people who supported you in reaching your goal.

But if there are still items on your bucket list, you need to get back to work. A successful life isn't a one and done kind of thing. It's striving for a string of victories along the way. Bo Eason, NFL football player turned award winning actor and playwright, tells us what living a victorious life looks like.

I remember when Michael Jordan was winning those six championships for the Bulls in the nineties. He would briefly put his arms above his head in celebration and then his hands would drop. You could see it on his face. The celebration was over—he was on to next year.

In the NFL, every win is short lived. The highest achievers don't celebrate long. They raise their hands in celebration, they hug their teammates, and then the next question is, "How do we do this again? Next game? Next year?"

After you celebrate and are ready to rev up again, there are three things you need to do:

1. Update your vision statement. Go on another dream-conjuring retreat. You will add new dreams and abandon others that are no longer important to you.

2. Take inventory of your Victor's Code status. If you're off track, revisit the elements and adjust as needed.

   - Valor—Does your confidence need fortification? Are you keeping progress-stopping fears in check?
   - Vehemence—Do you need to revisit your affirmations? Is it time to invest in some training to stoke your passion and get your head back in the game?
   - Veracity—Are you speaking, living, and loving truth?
   - Vitality—Are you living a healthy life?
   - Vigor—Have the vigor vampires crept back into your circle of friends and associates? Do you need to rethink partnerships that are no longer working?

3. Ask yourself, "What lessons have I learned along the way?" Apply what you learned to your next run.

Our years in the NFL were few, but we learned many valuable lessons that continue to inform our journey. They correct us when we get off course. They warn us of dangers. They encourage us when we get down. They nip at our heels to keep us on track.

Those lessons are the Victor's Code, and we've never stopped living it. Let's talk about what it looks like in our lives now.

SECTION II:

THE REST OF THE STORY

When we met, it was hate at first sight. We were floor control managers (a.k.a. bouncers) at a bar. It was a way to pick up some extra cash during the off-season before fall tryouts. We were vying for a coveted position to play for the Philadelphia Eagles. Testy young men, wired for competition and confrontation, we did not like each other at all.

Then one night, a bar room brawl broke out. It was our job to break it up and bounce the instigators. Standing back to back, we did our job. We emerged from the battle, bloody, bruised, and brothers. Our friendship was forged. It's been forty years and we have had each other's back ever since.

As our friendship grew, we compared notes and learned we had a hell of a lot in common. We both grew up in Rust Belt, working-class neighborhoods. Our fathers were hard workers. Dennis's father valued hard work by the hour and the sweat of the brow. He wasn't crazy about Dennis missing work to play ball. Vince's dad, another hard worker, felt that the best way to raise a son was to be stingy with praise and liberal with criticism. They were tough on us, but they were always in our court. Our mothers were great athletes. Dennis's mom was a professional figure skater; Vince's mom a professional baseball player. They helped us hone our skills.

We also shared a willingness to do whatever it takes to accomplish our goals. Our youthful ambition was to play in the NFL. We were determined to make it happen.

There were obstacles—plenty of them. An army of naysayers, armed with facts and figures, threatened to take us down. Historical precedence was against us. After all, Vince was too old and inexperienced to play for the NFL, and Dennis was too small to play with the big guys on the offensive line. But we defied that cold logic. We made the NFL, and with the skilled coaching of Dick Vermeil, we helped the team make history.

We've traveled many miles since those days with the NFL, but we have not strayed far from the lessons we've learned. We applied those lessons to our business endeavors and our personal lives. The Code was formed as much from the lessons learned from failure as the victories enjoyed in success.

Here's what that journey looked like.

Vulnerable to Invincible

Vince Papale

Year-round fitness was just not on the radar for most of the guys on the Eagles team. They figured that they had spent months getting pounded, they were going to use the offseason to relax. Not me. I planned to be the best conditioned player on the field.

I worked out like a demon. Dennis and I would show up at Veterans Stadium to work out and would stay until the trainers kicked us out. I pumped iron until I boosted my bench press from 180 to 296 pounds.

My plan worked. I wound up signing contracts for three straight years. I was voted special teams captain by my teammates and Man of the Year by the Eagles in 1978. Then it happened.

We were playing the Baltimore Colts. I was doing well, but Vermeil benched me. I was recovering from an off-season shoulder surgery. Coach didn't want to risk further damage to my shoulder. I begged to go back into the game. Unfortunately for me, he let me. During a punt takedown,

I dislocated my good shoulder. That was it. I couldn't lift my arm.

I wasn't cut right away. NFL teams can't cut you if you're injured while playing. I was put on injured reserve, and somehow that was worse. I lingered around the locker room. I felt like a leper. In those days, nobody wanted to hang with a guy who was hurt. It's as if they might catch an injury just by standing too close.

I was still getting paid, but I couldn't practice with the team. I rehabbed hard for more than two months until I finally felt strong enough to play. Once I was given a pass to go back on the field, I was released. Just like that, I was fired.

My heart broke. I felt sick to my stomach. I felt fear. No other team was going to pick up a thirty-three-year-old special teams player, especially not one who had missed most of the season with a bum shoulder.

I had just built a house and had no idea how I was going to pay for it, but money was not my most pressing concern. For three years I'd been riding a wave of popularity that granted me access to a life I had never imagined. I was invited to luncheons in the city's finest hotels. I was asked to speak to rooms full of successful people. I had been profiled in *Sports Illustrated*. I'd been on *The Mike Douglas Show*, the most popular TV talk show of the day. People stopped me in the street for an autograph or to tell me they were loyal fans. All of this was because of my well-known journey from the sandlots to the NFL. Without a team, I was just a guy who used to play.

In the past, I was the one who hosted team parties. Now, my former teammates didn't even bother to let me know where they'd be celebrating their wins. Fame is fickle. I learned that lesson well.

Football has brought me incredible joy, but not without consequences. It took a toll on my body, my emotions, and on my relationships, too. I had lost my first marriage due to my commitment to football.

Sandy, my wife at the time, enjoyed being on the arm of one of Philly's most popular athletes. She was now the wife of a guy looking for a job to try to make ends meet. My second marriage fell apart.

The next decade was a blur. I tried sales and marketing for Gold's Gym and for the *Philadelphia Star*. I was a sportscaster for a radio show. Nothing seemed to be a good fit.

I eventually ended up with a decent job working for U.S. Healthcare as a sales trainer and motivational speaker. I made some extra money on the side as a fitness trainer to the company's top executives. My focus was getting my body and emotions into tip-top shape.

It was at one of my speaking engagements that I met the love of my life, Janet Cantwell. She immediately caught my eye. She was petite, blond, and athletic. Come to find out, Janet was also a former professional athlete. She had been a member of the U.S. women's Olympic gymnastics team from 1970 to 1973 and went on to be an Olympic gymnastics coach. Janet was attractive, strong, and independent—impossible to ignore. It took a few months before we went on our first date, but it didn't take me long to fall in love with her.

As Janet and I got serious about our relationship, she asked, "Why are you so angry?" Of course, I got defensive. I was putting on a good show, but she wasn't buying it. Inside, I was in turmoil, carrying the resentment of not finishing a chapter in my life according to the script I had written. My football and TV career were in the toilet. I was bouncing from job to job. I was sabotaging relationships. Debt was breathing down my neck. I was not answering my phone for fear that it was a bill collector calling.

Janet helped me get my head on straight. I got out of debt and on track financially again. I gave up my wanton ways. I started to build a life again.

We were married in 1993. Five months later, our daughter, Gabriella, was born. Three years after that we had a son, Vincent. Talk about victories. An Olympic gold medal and a Super Bowl ring together could not compare to my best victory ever—Janet!

Life was sweet. I had a beautiful family. Janet's real estate business was thriving. I had transferred to a good job with Sallie Mae, the student loan company. I didn't need anything else.

I had my health too, or so I thought. I started having some digestive issues, and Janet insisted I get a checkup. She threatened to trade me in for a couple of thirty-year-olds if I didn't get one. Thank God she kept pestering me. She saved my life.

A cancerous polyp in my gut was just waiting to pop its cork and ravage my body with its deadly cells. Are you freaking kidding me? Cancer? No way! That was without a doubt the toughest non-football-related hit I ever took. It shook me to the core physically and emotionally.

I'd look at my kids, three and six, and start crying. Am I going to see them grow up? Is this it? One day, Janet, in her typical unfiltered way, said, "Vince, get your head out of your butt, stop feeling sorry for yourself, and let's kick this colon cancer thing once and for all!"

As a team, we beat it. I'm now fifteen years cancer-free. I'm a fierce advocate for colorectal cancer awareness. When I speak at events, I do a one-minute PSA. I tell my audience to get tested, kidding them, "You never know what you will find up there. The last time I got checked they found my father's shoe." Boom! If it hadn't been for Janet insisting that I get tested, I would not be here. She recently received the Guardian Angel of the Year Award from a prominent cancer awareness organization. No argument there.

I was still the guy who *used* to play pro ball, but that didn't bother me anymore. I had a life. I had a wife, a decent job, and two great kids. Football wasn't even on my radar.

In 2002, my life changed again when I got a call from the producer of NFL films. Before every Monday night football game, they aired "Distant Replay" pieces—segments about former players. They asked me to do one, and also interviewed Denny Franks, Jim Murray, and Ron Jaworski. It was great fun.

My segment was in honor of the twenty-fifth anniversary of *Rocky*. The *Rocky* films were big in Philly. They starred and were directed by local boy Sylvester Stallone. The series is the story of Rocky Balboa, a small-time boxer, and his unlikely rise to fame as a world champion.

The segment included footage of me running the streets of Philly spliced with shots of Rocky running up the steps of the art museum.

Coach Vermeil was interviewed and reinforced the metaphor: he talked about how I represented the city and how fans could envision me punching sides of beef the same way Rocky had. There was a segment of me going crazy on the sidelines and wearing my Who's Nuts? t-shirt.

The bitterness for how the Eagles had dumped me faded. I was proud of what I had accomplished. I was happy that my kids got to see it.

The next morning my phone was ringing off the hook. Hollywood was calling: several producers wanted to make a movie about my life. For six months, Janet and I listened to pitches and promises. This was a new experience for us. We were not sure who to go with or even what we were looking for.

We finally settled on 10x10 entertainment, owned by producer Ken Mok. Ken shopped the NFL tape to several studios, but no one was interested without a script. Over the next year, a young screenwriter named Brad Gann and I spent hours on the phone, recapping the most important moments of my life. Finally, in October, 2004, the script for *Invincible* was finished and auctioned off.

The movie didn't become a reality until the spring of 2005, when Mark Wahlberg decided to take the starring role. Mark was perfect for the part. He had lived my story. He was a poor kid from nowhere who had beaten the odds to make something of himself. He remains a well-respected Hollywood actor.

That movie has inspired many people, which means so much to me. It has been used to inspire sales professionals and soldiers. In 2007, The Appalachian State University football team viewed it the night before their surprise upset against Michigan. It's a David and Goliath story that has inspired a lot of Davids to pick up that rock and sling it. Giants can be toppled. Challenges can be overcome.

Janet and I now live in Cherry Hill, New Jersey, with our children, Gabriella and Vinny. I remain a diehard Philadelphia Eagles fan and serve as Secretary/Treasurer of the Philadelphia chapter of the NFL Alumni Association.

In 2011, I launched my own personal brand, a training and motivational system called Invincible. It's based on a system outlined in my first book, *Be Invincible*, which Janet and I co-authored. The Invincible brand is about building backbone. It's about inspiring courage in those who are facing an adversary—negative family members, poor health, a job loss, a seemingly impossible goal—anything that puts or keeps you down. It has opened doors for me to speak all over the nation for major corporations, school groups, and even at a training camp for Navy SEALs.

These days, Dennis and I are applying the Victor's Code to our latest conquest—inspiring and coaching others to enjoy their last laugh.

I'm back, and I'm invincible!

Busting Through Barriers

Dennis Franks

It was 1979, the third game of a 2–0 season. I really believed that this was the year we'd make a deep playoff run. The previous year, the team voted me the most valuable special teams player. I was a wedge-buster, baby. Crazy, courageous, and effective. Life was good.

Then, one dark day, it all came crashing down. Coach Vermeil called me into his office. He told me I was being released and picked up by the Detroit Lions. The coach had tears in his eyes; it was hard for him, too. My heart sank like a punctured balloon. I could only take in the news and thank the coach for the opportunity to play with the Philadelphia Eagles. I didn't want to make a scene. I knew not to burn any bridges.

I had to close down my house in Philly for the season, gather my things, and catch a plane to Motor City within three days. Upon arrival, I went to the Lions' main office complex and had a meeting with the head coach, Monte Clarke. Clarke was a large man, a former offensive tackle for the San Francisco 49ers. The first words out of his mouth? "So you're Dennis Franks? How tall are you and how much do you weigh?" I felt like a piece of merchandise being sized up. I was miserable.

During the very first game against the Falcons, I got into three fights with my own teammates. I was knocked halfway down the field because one of my new teammates missed his assigned play. I confronted him on the sideline. "What the hell happened?"

"I missed the block. No big deal," he responded. "We're going to lose anyway."

What?! I punched him in the head and fight number one started. We were broken up and cooled down. It wasn't five minutes later that another stupid lackluster play happened and I yelled, "Hey, does your husband play?" Bam, fight number two broke out.

His buddy mouthed off and pushed me—bam: fight number three.

They say that discretion is the better part of valor. Well, I had plenty of valor, but not a lot of discretion. Coach Clarke grabbed me and said, "What the f**k are you doing?"

"You have a bunch of losers on your team," I snarled.

To my surprise, Coach named me Captain of Special Teams the following week. Sometimes valor does win over discretion. Despite the honor, my heart wasn't in the game anymore. I was going through the motions. I lost my love of playing football. It was over. The following year, I left the team.

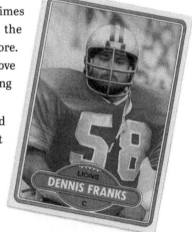

It was time to go back to Philadelphia and begin my life in the world of business. I felt confident that I could make this transition. Hey, I was an All-American. I studied economics at the University of Michigan, for Pete's sake. I had contacts and played five years in the NFL. Certainly someone would hire me as an executive. Someone would give me that corner office and pay me six figures. Right?

Wrong!

After what seemed like 100 interviews, the only offer I got was to start at an entry level sales position. Making it even worse, they offered to pay $20,000—six figures less than I made in the NFL.

Starting over taught me a couple of valuable lessons.

1. Life is not fair.

2. Even if you make it in one area, you're going to have to prove yourself again and again in other areas.

I had to pay the bills, so I went to work with my former sports agent, Mark Stewart. I learned the sports agent industry fast. Back then, it was unregulated—like the wild, wild west. It was about spending money, making promises, and babying diva athletes. I got tired of that fast.

But the most destructive part of it were the parties. I knew how to party and drank my fair share of alcohol, but this was a whole new level. Night after night, I partied with pro athletes and entertainers. At these parties, I was introduced to cocaine. It seemed all the successful people were using it. Crazy. Impressionable. I wanted to hang out with the successful people, so why not use it too?

Next thing you know, I started experimenting. Within weeks, I became a frequent user, then an addict. Parties were no longer just a nightly thing. They lasted for days. I was losing control.

It took a near-death experience to wake me up. After partying for thirty-six hours nonstop, my heart was pumping so hard it felt like it was going to explode. A friend walked me for hours until I settled down. On that walk, I made a decision to get my life back on track. Breaking a cocaine habit is not easy, but I was determined to get it done—cold turkey.

Things began to happen. Out of nowhere, my former roommate from the Detroit Lions, Dave, showed up in Philadelphia for a tryout with the

Eagles. I let him stay with me. Dave pointed out that I had grown fat, depressed, and surly. He suggested I try a milkshake diet that his mom was selling.

It was easy—three shakes a day and lots of water. No food for fourteen days. He made me clean the beer, soda, and chips out of my kitchen. By day three of my milkshake diet, I wanted to bite someone's head off, but I hung in there. In twelve weeks, I lost fifty pounds.

Everyone was asking about my dramatic weight loss. I began referring people to Dave's mom to buy the shakes. I helped his mom make about $5,000 through referrals. She called to thank me for my help and suggested that I start selling the stuff. Overnight, I became an entrepreneur and a network marketer selling health and weight loss through Cambridge Plan International.

Life was good. I was making big money selling shakes by day and having fun making music by night. Music was a creative release for me. My friend, Mark Stewart (the sports agent) also represented entertainers under his label Tech Records. He convinced me to perform a rap written for the Philadelphia Eagles called "The Eagles Battle Cry." That led to a recording and a gig rapping the song before the 1980 championship game against the Dallas Cowboys. I rapped and danced with the Liberty Bells, the Eagles cheerleaders. Not a bad gig. While I rapped and danced, my beautiful girlfriend, Nancy Haslett, was outside the stadium selling my records. As always, she supported me in my dreams. That beautiful woman eventually became my wife.

Marrying Nancy was one of the best decisions I've ever made. I've learned the value of having a life partner who will stand by you in sickness and in health; for richer or poorer; come what may. Indeed, Nancy and I had some unforeseen dark days to face together.

Cambridge Plan International was cruising along. It was fun. Nancy had become a Playboy Bunny and got me a gig helping Playboy Bunnies stay at their working weight. This got us a lot of attention. We were among the fastest-growing network marketers (direct selling professionals) in the nation. Network marketers have distribution rights to products and services that they promote through word of mouth rather than through traditional advertising channels— any product that comes to you directly from a sales person, not from a store.

One day, we got some really bad news. A woman died, supposedly after losing thirty pounds on the Cambridge diet. The company chose not to dignify the rumor with a response, sure the news would blow over. Unfortunately, their competitors kept the rumor alive, even though it was eventually proven that the diet had nothing to do with her death. Sales tanked. Commissions dropped like lead.

Cambridge went into Chapter 11 bankruptcy and my commission checks were held until they reorganized. Nancy and I had a loyal customer base and were able to sustain a pretty decent income. Impressed with the stability of our retail base even in the face of this public relations crisis, founder and CEO Vaughn Feather asked me to come work at corporate. So the next thing I know, I'm the vice president of a major network marketing company—great news! The bad news? They were still in Chapter 11.

I was traveling from Philly to Monterey, California, every other week and working 24/7. It was not easy on Nancy. She was pregnant and caring for our two-year-old daughter, Lauren, but we both knew this was our best route to get back to the top. So we did what we had to do.

Our hard work paid off. Cambridge Plan International paid back all their debt and we were on track again. But darker days were ahead.

Things seemed good. I moved the family to Monterey and was making great money. I had an amazing wife and our family was growing. Then, one day, sitting in my office, in walk three men—two local authorities and an FBI agent. Their first words were, "Dennis Franks? You are under arrest for the sale of illegal drugs."

I was in shock. In the space of about ten minutes, I went from being at the top of my game to crushed under the weight of a thousand uncertainties.

It had been five years since I had touched a drug. I had certainly purchased a lot of cocaine and shared some with friends when I was using, but I never sold drugs. Unfortunately, my name was found in the sales ledger of someone who was busted for cocaine distribution. I was guilty by association. The outcome? I was given a one-year sentence. I had to stay in a halfway house on weekends and do community service.

That year seemed like an eternity, but the dark days passed. Life goes on. I regret the pain that those dark days inflicted on my family, but I don't regret the lessons learned. Failure is an excellent teacher.

The big lesson? Choose your partners and friends wisely. Your team can either lift you up or take you down.

I also learned that failing doesn't make you a failure. Think about Thomas Edison, one of the most successful innovators in American history. He failed big time and often. When asked about his many missteps in attempting to invent a light bulb, Edison replied, "I have not failed—I've just found 10,000 ways that will not work."

Me too. My many failures helped me identify what worked and what didn't. They helped me identify my strengths and my weaknesses. There's no teacher like experience. I had the book knowledge from my years at the University of Michigan, but I got my real education from life.

I had several business ventures after the Cambridge years. I learned about myself and about the systems that worked and that didn't, at least for me.

Nancy and I, with a few close friends, opened a Mailbox Etc. franchise that eventually grew into a Master Franchise that oversaw several locations. These were the UPS stores of that time. As a franchise owner, I learned that brick-and-mortar businesses are confining. You have to be at your business or thinking about it 24/7. I don't like to be confined.

I was also a partner in an industrial company with a really good man who was willing to pay me what I was worth. Though I learned a lot and made some good money, it wasn't a good fit.

The business modality that fit me best was network marketing. It was location-independent, it was inexpensive to get started, the industry had huge earning potential, and I had the touch. I loved that it let me work when I wanted to work. I liked the people the industry attracted.

Yes, you had to sift through some scoundrels, just like in any line of work. But some of the most visionary, upright, and caring people I've ever met I found through my work in network marketing.

I tried a few different companies. I was part of a skin care company called NuSkin—I can still remember the terrified look I got from those women when this hulking NFL guy lurched forward to slap some lotion on their face. Nah. Not my thing.

I also was part of a company called Microdiet. The Microdiet offered a decent weight loss program and marketed through infomercials. Thousands joined the business and thousands failed. There was no training system in place. Without a training to support my new distributors, I was building a business on shifting sand.

One big drawback to network marketing is the multi-level marketing compensation (MLM) system, which is standard for the direct selling industry. It requires a superstar effort. You have to build a team of thousands to make any serious money. Recruiting was not a problem for me. I had lots of contacts and, having played in the NFL, credibility, too. Most people don't have those advantages. If you happened to attach to a superstar, you might make it, but only if that superstar was willing to invest time to teach you—otherwise you were adrift. Though I recruited hundreds, the dropout rate was staggering.

I was getting disillusioned with the industry until I got a call from a man named JR Ridinger. Ridinger had gotten my number from a friend of a friend of a friend of a friend of a friend. He was relentless in his follow-up, even though I wasn't interested. To get him off my back, I decided to meet with him. I was going to tell him, straight up, "No thank you."

I was headed to a golf tournament in Avalon, New Jersey, and agreed to meet him at an office of a friend in Ocean City. I told him he had thirty minutes, period. Little did I know that what he would share with me that day would captivate me for the next twenty-five years.

So I met the one and only JR Ridinger. We spent a few minutes getting to know each other. I liked the guy; we had a lot in common. He was from South Jersey. He was an exceptional athlete in multiple sports through high school. He went on to Gettysburg College where he excelled in wrestling. He was eventually inducted into their Hall of Fame.

Then he said something that made me lean in: "I'm going to change the network marketing industry." He told me he was sick and tired of the way people perceived the industry. He told me he wanted to offer multiple product lines to weather the market swings and trends. This product and service diversity would offer something for every distributor and every customer. He called it "the Mall Without Walls."

He wasn't going to manufacture anything. He was going to broker products from manufacturers and service vendors. They had to be high quality and offered at a competitive price. The products would be things that customers wanted, not just high-priced crap that only distributors would be willing to buy. Product brokering would allow him to change as the marketplace changed.

He had deconstructed the old math of multilevel marketing and reconstructed a new compensation system in which the average person could succeed. I leaned in further. He showed me the math—math based on forty years of direct selling statistics. It was brilliant. Game on.

Then he reached into his pocket and pulled out one of his products—a cheap little piece of jewelry called Lusterbond. Say what? He also dropped the bomb that he had very little money to capitalize this vision. I could have walked away at that moment, but I didn't. Why? I didn't buy into the lint-covered jewelry he pulled from his pocket. I didn't buy into his bank account. I bought into JR's vision. He said, "This will work because this is an idea whose time has come and I am going to make it work." I believed him.

I became one of the first distributors with this company and, eventually, a corporate executive. The good news? I was now an Executive Vice President for a promising start up. The bad news? They only had a few crappy products and little money.

Partnering with JR in the development of Market America/Shop.com was one of the best decisions I've ever made. Together with JR, the brilliant visionary at the helm, our corporate team has built a business in which the average person with a dream has a path to success.

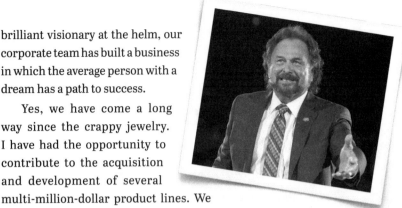

Yes, we have come a long way since the crappy jewelry. I have had the opportunity to contribute to the acquisition and development of several multi-million-dollar product lines. We now offer thousands of exclusive, high-quality products. We also offer millions of affiliate products. Then came Shop.com. This website provides the sophisticated technology required to get the products to the customer while tracking compensation for the independent contractor and the consumer. Market America and Shop.com now exclusively offer the Shopping Annuity, which converts spending into earning. (Learn more about this from JR Ridinger himself in the Hall of Fame.)

I have traveled the world educating and motivating an international sales force. I have helped grow this company from hardly any money in the bank to a multibillion-dollar enterprise. I am honored and grateful to have had that opportunity.

Assisting with the growth of Market America/Shop.com has been exhilarating, but what I am most proud of is the people I've helped: I have empowered truck drivers, construction workers, single moms and dads, frustrated professionals, and underpaid service workers to earn what they are truly worth, not what others have told them they are worth. Watching my team exceed expectations and earn a respectable income working part-time from home—that's why I do what I do.

I have been blessed in so many ways. I have that house on the hill—a couple in fact. I have some big, fancy cars. But at the end of the day, my treasure is the love of my wife and my two amazing daughters, Lauren and Katie. I now have two great son-in-laws, too. Best of all, I have Izzy, my precious granddaughter.

Glean what you can from my life. It is both a cautionary tale and an application of the Victor's Code.

SECTION III:

THE VICTOR'S CODE HALL OF FAME

"Heroes are ordinary people who make themselves extraordinary."

—Gerard Way

Visiting the Pro Football Hall of Fame in Canton, Ohio, is a lifelong dream for so many fans. With every step through the museum's halls, you sense the ghosts of the greats who are no longer on this earth but continue to inspire us. You relive some of the greatest moments in football history captured on video and film.

It's a shrine that honors those who had a vision to play ball and play with passion—those who had the last laugh. We are blessed that the "Last Laugh" photo found a home among the Eagles memorabilia. Okay—we admit we get a big kick out of the fact that it's displayed right above a photo of the Dallas Cowboys.

Given this legacy, it's fitting that we have a Victor's Code Hall of Fame. We asked successful (and very busy) people to share not only what they have achieved in life, but the challenges they overcame to get there. Each one has their own story, but you will find some things they all have in common: the elements of the Victor's Code have played a role in their journey.

They knew what they passionately wanted to achieve. They stayed the course until victory was in hand.

Here is your chance to learn from them.

THE LAST LAUGH

Above: Big recognition night for Dennis and Nancy.

Left: Dennis's rookie season with the Philadelphia Eagles in 1975.

Above: Philadelphia Eagles offensive line, 1978.

Above: Franks family photo in Captiva, Florida.

Above: Game day with the
Philadelphia Eagles at the Linc.

Above: Dennis playing American
Airlines Arena in Miami, Florida.

Left: Celebrating Vince's win over colon cancer, 2001.

Below: As a team, Vince and Janet make the impossible possible, 2012.

Above: So proud of our invincible family, Gabriella, Janet, and Vinny! 2017.

Right: Janet's family, the Cantwells. She's the oldest of nine.

Left: Very proud to support our law enforcement!

Above: Celebrating Vince's greatest catch...Janet!

Above: With Coach Vermeil at the *Invincible* premiere, the man who started it all.

Above: Celebrating our dreams of making the team with our dads, Don and Kingie, in Dallas for the Eagles vs. Cowboys game in 1976.

Above: The ultimate team at Super Bowl XLI in Miami in 2007. Indianapolis Colts vs. Chicago Bears.

Above: Toasting 40 years of friendship.

Above: Vince and Dennis teaming up with NASCAR at the Coca Cola 600 in Charlotte.

Pat Croce

"You can only accept what is. When you fiercely accept how the universe unfolds, you see it as something you need. The universe isn't doing it to you, it's doing it for you. Whatever comes your way, fiercely accept it as a lesson you need to learn."

PAT'S VICTORIES

Pat started out as an athletic trainer for the Philadelphia 76ers. Eventually, he became president and an owner. Under his guidance, the 76ers went from last place to the NBA finals. He appeared on the cover of *Success Magazine* as the first trainer to rise to an ownership position with a professional sports team.

Pat founded Sports Physical Therapists in 1984 and grew the business into a chain of forty centers spanning eleven states. He served as administrative director of the Sports Medicine Clinic of Haverford Community Hospital and has been profiled in *Inc. Magazine* and *Sales & Marketing Management*.

He was one of the four judges for ABC's reality television series *American Inventor*, served as a taekwondo commentator for the 2004 Summer Olympics, and has served as an NBA commentator on NBC. He also hosted a syndicated TV show, *Pat Croce, Moving In*.

Today, Pat is the owner of the St. Augustine Pirate and Treasure Museum and the pirate-themed Rum Barrel restaurant. He owns and operates, in conjunction with the University of Florida, the Colonial Quarter living history museum in St. Augustine. He serves on the board of directors for Movitas, a mobile technology company focused on the hospitality industry. He financed and served on the expedition that located the shipwrecks of explorer Sir Francis Drake.

Pat is also a prolific author and has written or co-written books about everything from sports medicine to pirates.

THE LAST LAUGH

My first last laugh was getting rejected by the Philadelphia Eagles. I naïvely knocked on their door and asked, "Do you have a physical therapist on staff?"

They said, "No."

I told them, "That is the job I want to apply for." The head trainer slammed the door in my face.

There is another V—the "voice" in the head. It can be so destructive. I could have walked away from that experience and let the voice accuse me: *I'm no good. I can't do this. It won't work.* But I didn't. That rejection fueled me. It set in motion an entirely different path for me. I accepted the no. "Okay. Maybe I'm not ready." I pulled myself up by the bootstraps. I worked a little harder and took some more courses. I continued to build relationships and strive for my dream.

I have learned to fiercely accept a "No." I don't put myself down when I get a rejection. I consider it direction. "This is not where I need to go now." Eventually, I became a conditioning coach for the Flyers and the Sixers. I went on to be part owner of the Sixers and president of the franchise.

You can only accept what is. When you fiercely accept how the universe unfolds, you see it as something you need. The universe isn't doing it to you, it's doing it for you. Whatever comes your way, fiercely accept it as a lesson you need to learn.

VISION

Nothing happens without vision. Nothing. Without vision, you will spend your life fulfilling other people's dreams. In my book, *Lead or Get Off the Pot*, I outline a vision breakdown:

- It starts with a dream, a vision, an intention, something you want to achieve.
- Break that vision down into time-sensitive goals.
- If that vision doesn't have a time correlated to it, then it's only a wish. Everyone has wishes. No—it must have time-sensitive goals.
- Take each of those goals and break them down further into strategies. How am I going to achieve this goal?
- Take each strategy and break it down even further into action steps. These are the items that go on your to-do list.

You must believe you can accomplish your vision. Not just hope so. Hope is a mask of fear. When you say, "I hope I can get something done," or, "I hope I can do this," it's bullshit. It's a pretty mask on your fear. You're really saying, "I am afraid that I might not be able to do this."

Somewhere on that rainbow from the vision to the to-do list, people fall off. Vince Papale, Dennis Franks, the people in the Hall of Fame all rode the rainbow. They made it all the way. They achieved their vision. They might have used different strategies or encountered different detours, but they made it.

Detours are just the universe unfolding. Success is accepting that detour. It is being present and doing your best RIGHT NOW. That is how you wow the universe. In Zen, there is a proverb: "How you do anything is how you do everything."

VALOR

If you fiercely accept circumstances, they can be a catalyst for change.

On February 20th, 1998, I had a meeting for the 76ers season ticket holders. This was my rookie year as president of the franchise. I had promised to accomplish many things. I was going to give them updates and hear their concerns, comments, and questions.

We had started the season off well, but then things got bad. We had lost the last five games. We had thirteen wins and thirty-nine losses. It was an awful time to go in front of the season ticket holders—my customers. It took courage.

The meeting turned into a bloodbath. They were screaming, yelling, and cursing at me. "The coach can't coach. The GM can't evaluate talent. The players can't play." They wanted me to trade every player except rookie Allen Iverson. It was embarrassing and painful.

After the meeting, I'm making my way to the exit tunnel. About two dozen fans try to block my exit. I'm thinking, *Oh no.* I can handle myself pretty well. I'm a fourth degree black belt in Taekwondo. I'm a street fighter. But a gang of Philly fans? I'm going to get my ass kicked. To my surprise, instead of jumping me, they thanked me for listening and caring.

The next day, the press had a field day. The bloodbath was broadcast on ESPN—Fans in the Stands news. You might as well have taken my pants down and publicly beat me with a belt across the butt.

That was the turning point for the franchise. It caused a 180-degree shift. I did fire the coach and general manager. By my third season, we were in the playoffs, and by the fifth, we were in the finals.

The passion of the fans created a ripple in our ocean. The ocean was our passion for winning. That ripple was strong enough to bring about the changes needed to set our winning streak in motion.

Valor is standing up and doing what you think is right, even if taking that stand causes pain and embarrassment.

VITALITY

Vitality is energy. Without energy, even if you have a great vision, you won't last.

It starts with getting a good night's rest. I get 7–8 hours of sleep each night. I am a big believer in nourishing myself with good sleep. Some say they can survive on 4–5 hours. I'm not about surviving. I'm about thriving. I believe you need 7–8 hours to energize you for the other 16 hours. You must be ON when you greet the world. If you are tired when you pick up the phone or respond to an email, you might express something you will regret for the rest of your life.

I have a morning routine. My routine wakes up my mind. I get out of bed. As soon as my feet hit the ground, I feel the energy flowing through me. I clap my hands, rub them together, and say, "Today is going to be a great day." I take that energy from the earth—it flows from my feet right up to the crown of my head.

I love when my feet hit the ground between 4–4:30 a.m. I have a cup of coffee. I take the dog outside for a walk. I journal and do some Chinese writing. From there I work out for an hour. After I work out, I shower and eat breakfast. I then meditate. Boom! I'm ready for the day.

Even though I am retired now, I still have this routine. By 9 a.m., my body is ready. My mind is ready. I have the energy I need to face the day. In the afternoon, I take a ten-minute power nap. I look like Grandpa Munster laying in a coffin. I nap just long enough for that blood to cross the blood-brain barrier.

Regarding food, I'm Italian. I was raised on pasta. I love it, but I can't eat as much I used to. I eat three meals a day. I rarely snack. If I do snack, it's a small snack like fruit or carrots. If I have something like potato chips, it's a handful, not a full bag. I don't eat late. I don't go to bed with a full stomach. I'm 90% gluten-free. I eat nourishing food and have protein with my meals. My favorite protein is fresh fish. I have restaurants in Key West. That's where you get fresh fish. I drink alcohol at happy hour, but I don't drink after that.

I believe in moderation. I don't worry about my diet. I try to be fully present when I am eating. That's the problem with a lot of people; they just stuff their face. They haven't even tasted the first helping and they can't wait to get to the second. That's why there are so many overweight people.

Spirituality also affects your energy. You have to know that the Divine One is in your corner. That stokes fierce acceptance when challenges come, like Hurricane Irma. God knows the plan. We're just players on this field. God knows the outcome. So go with it. That gives you more energy.

The voice in the head affects vitality too. Look around you. You will see people who are not even working that hard, but they're dead tired because their mind is beating them up.

VIGOR

To deal with the things that drain emotional energy, you need to go to the seed of the emotion—that voice in the head, the chatterbox. You have a thought. You infuse that thought with energy and consciousness. It becomes an emotion. That emotion turns into a reaction—like igniting a powder keg.

We all have karmic DNA, and that affects our reactions. That karmic DNA can come from our parents or ancestors. The best way to change negative emotional energy is to give it space. If you are angry, breathe.

Anger, disappointment, and being upset are fear-based. That is not who you truly are. It's a thought. Your thoughts aren't you. They are just thoughts. Let them go. When you hold onto them, you infuse them with more energy. That voice in your head says, "You know what that person said about me?" The thought keeps going. You begin to create a mind map and add more energy to it. It becomes an emotion and creates a negative ripple in your pond.

We all have negative thoughts, unless maybe you're the Dalai Lama,

Jesus Christ, Buddha, or Gandhi. We all have negative thoughts, but they're not you. Let them go. I work on my biceps and my quadriceps, but the most important muscle I work on is my LET IT GO muscle.

VERACITY

My late father used to say, "If you don't ask, the answer is always no." So, many times, I've asked and was told no. But I don't hear the no. When I asked Harold Katz, the former owner of the 76ers, if I could buy 10% of the team, he said, "No. When I sell the team, it will be all or nothing." I didn't hear no, I heard "all or nothing." I came back forty-eight hours later and offered, "I want to buy the team from you. All of it." He said, "No. When I sell the team, it is going to be for about 125 million dollars. I'm not ready to sell yet." I didn't hear no. I heard "125 million dollars." The first rule of negotiation—he who says the first number loses. Take "no" as the information you need. It's a learning experience.

VEHEMENCE

You need to believe in yourself vehemently. Not that you're better or worse than someone else. That's ego. Believe in yourself and know your purpose. That's all.

When you believe in yourself, understand your purpose, and do your best work NOW, you create high vibrational energy. You activate the law of attraction. For example, you could be waiting tables. When you believe in yourself, know your purpose, and do your best work NOW, people will notice. "Hey, look at that waiter. What a great attitude. Look at the smile. We should give him a job."

Passion (or vehemence) is embers. When you stoke those embers into a fire, you can heat the world.

VICTORY

I have always been one who believed in celebrating the little victories. I felt that celebrating the small wins stoked the embers of passion. I am now of the faith that when you are present NOW, that is success. Victory is not a future achievement.

As the Bhagavad-Gita—one of the greatest books outside the Bible—says, "Do not be attached to the fruits of your labor." Do not be attached to the fruits of your actions. The action you take today is not about achieving a win later. It is about winning now—in the present. Do your best now, because now is all you have. Today is not a means to an end. Today is the end. This is all we have. When you realize that, the wins become even more glorious.

Cosmo DeNicola

"Attack everything with the expectation of winning. Don't make excuses. Believe you're going to win every time. Play to that standard. Does that mean you're always going to win? No. But do everything in your power to win."

COSMO'S VICTORIES

Cosmo's extensive portfolio includes the three-time world champion Philadelphia Soul Arena Football League team (he co-owns the team with Ron Jaworski, former Philadelphia Eagles player and analyst for ESPN; Dick Vermeil, legendary coach of the Philadelphia Eagles and the 2000 St. Louis Rams Super Bowl team, motivational speaker, and football analyst; and Marcus Colston and Jahri Evans, New Orleans Saints Super Bowl winners); MKS&D Talent Management (a firm that has managed Tony Award and Grammy-nominated musicians and actors in film, television, and theater for more than thirty years); Steinberg Sports and Entertainment (in partnership with sports agent Leigh Steinberg; this business merges the worlds of sports, media, entertainment, branding, and cause-related marketing); Chicken Soup for the Soul Entertainment; Amtech Software (the leading worldwide provider of software and hardware for the packaging industry), and several other businesses. He also does business in health care, technology, and public relations.

His primary pursuit in business and in life is to improve efficiency and productivity. He is on the board of several institutions, including The Humpty Dumpty Institute, The Arena Football League (AFL), and St. John Vianney Church.

THE LAST LAUGH

I am the son of two Italian immigrant families who came to the U.S. after World War II. We settled in northeast Philadelphia, a very humble inner-city neighborhood. I had a traditional 1950s–60s upbringing. My father was a carpenter, my mother a stay-at-home mom. My parents provided a loving and positive home. I was made to feel special. When you feel that you are special, it's a crime not to give all you have.

I was the first person to go to college in my family. I attended Temple University, going to school nights and weekends all year round. I worked a full-time job during the day and a part-time job on weekends. Despite my commitments, I finished my degree in four years. In my sophomore year, at nineteen years old, I married my sweetheart, Janet. We have been together now for forty-three years.

I love working. I am driven by competing. Every job I've ever had, there was an element of competition. I wanted to flip burgers faster than anyone else or make the chicken or whatever faster and better. I wasn't always competing against other people, but I was always competing against myself. I sought my personal best every time.

I was blessed with mentors. For whatever reason, some older guys I worked with saw something in me that made them take me under their wing. You can get a DNA test that tells you what ethnicities you are. If you did a DNA test on my business acumen, every one of those mentors would show up. They are part of me and I carry them with me wherever I go.

My first business was an accounting firm. I did taxes and accounting for small businesses and individuals. April 1, 1981, on my twenty-sixth birthday, I started a company called Amtech Software, which is still in business thirty-seven years later.

As a teenager, I dreamed of playing professional football. I also wanted to be a doctor. Neither of those dreams came true. Forty-five years later, I gave the commencement speech at the Fox School of Business at Temple University. It is one of the best business schools in the country. The title was "I Went to Temple to be a Doctor and Play Football, and I did Neither." My point: it's okay to change your goals. As long as you're fearless in your pursuit of those goals, you will be okay. I didn't play football, but I ended up owning a professional football team, the Philadelphia Soul. I didn't become a doctor, but I ended up owning three healthcare companies.

I no longer live in the old neighborhood, but I give homage to it. My high school recognized me in their Hall of Fame. Even though I never had an NFL career, I am in the City Hall All Stars Chapter of the Pennsylvania Sports Hall of Fame. I have received recognition for doing what I was born to do—work, love, care, and compete with passion.

Here's my last laugh: I had been in business about ten years when a recession hit in the early 90s. It was the first punch in the stomach since I had started my business. Sales of my product went flat. It was like someone turned off the spigot and I couldn't sell my product anymore. I was thinking about selling the house that I lived in with my two babies and my wife. We looked for economical housing so we could afford to weather the storm. I didn't let anyone on the outside see how scared I was, but it was very bad.

I am one who works through things, so I started thinking about products. How could I improve what I have and build a better product? I had this idea about a software solution for the packaging industry. Janet and I met with a marketing firm to pitch the product. I told them, "I'm excited about this product. I've done my research. I think it can transform our business." After my pitch, they excused themselves and left the room. The came back about ten minutes later to let me know the meeting was over. They told me my ideas for this new system were pipe dreams. They didn't want to waste their time working with me. They were sure I was going to fail. To put it politely, they threw us out of their office.

My wife and I looked at each other. Really? Was this possible? We laughed. My wife believes in me and I believe in her. We knew the product was going to be a success. No one was going to stop us.

The idea I had was a software system called Imaginera. Over the years, it has become an overwhelming success to the point of being the market leader in its niche. All our success in the areas of sports, entertainment, healthcare, and technology, as well as our humanitarian efforts, were funded by this product. At the end of the day, every good thing I've done I've been able to do because of the success of the product that they laughed at.

Years later, I was going to that same office building to shoot a video for my football team. My assistant, Natalie, was with me. I pointed to their door and said, "That's the firm." I'm not the type to go back and say, "Look what I did." I use rejection for motivation. It gave me a reason to succeed. It was my last laugh and I am still laughing.

VISION

I always knew I was different. By fifth grade, I thought that I was special, but by sixth grade, I knew that I was special. I saw the world with clarity. I recognized that opportunities are all around us, and they have the potential to affect our lives. Awareness of what was going on around me and clarity of vision allowed me to launch and develop an ever-growing portfolio of businesses.

Clarity is more than having 20/20 vision. It is being aware of opportunities, resources, and limitations. It's a deep understanding. When you have clarity, you can move forward confidently, expecting success.

Life doesn't go in a straight line. With clarity, you can make adjustments along the way. I started as a pre-med major, I transitioned into speech, then I transferred to accounting. That's okay. Once I was clear on my personal goals, I adjusted along the way.

VITALITY

Clarity applies to vitality, too. You need energy and vitality to perform. When you have clarity, you will know when your body needs a rest or you need to have a moment to meditate. You will know when you need to walk away from the table, change your diet, or resist that cocktail.

You will also be able to react to pain in your body and find a solution. I have had a few operations this past year on my eyes and knees. You can't live your life to the fullest and get the job done if there are physical limitations. Take care of the things you need to take care of. It is all about clarity and awareness.

VALOR

I'm a very sensitive person. I can come across as tough, I know, but I am really sensitive. I also seem extremely outgoing, but in reality, I am kind of shy.

In my early days, I was scared to death to make sales calls. The potential for rejection by strangers scared the living hell out of me. I had to push myself. I did a pretty good job of hiding it. Like they say, "Never let them see you sweat." Now, give me a microphone and a stage and you can't shut me up.

To succeed in business, you can't show fear. If you do, your customers and employees will see it; the bankers, the lawyers, and accountants will see it. It will affect your ability to lead.

Over time, I have become fearless. That valor or fearlessness is in part because of my mentors. When I was a young man in my 20s, one of mentors told me, "You are young enough to go bankrupt three times and still be a billionaire." I never had to go bankrupt and I am not a billionaire, but his words helped instill valor in me.

I have also had the safety net of my wife and my family. When you have a safety net, you don't fear failure. You can always go home. When you don't have a fear of falling back, when you are clear on what you want to achieve, you can move forward with confidence.

VEHEMENCE

The foundation of my vehemence or passion is that I am super organized. It's one of my biggest assets.

Like right now, I'm staring at three bins. Keep in mind I own several technology companies, so I have access to all sorts of tools to keep me organized. But I have these bins labeled today, tomorrow, and later. And, on the wall of my office, I have nine separate whiteboards. These tools help me compartmentalize. Each board reflects a different company and contains the small goals that have to be achieved. When they are achieved, they are erased.

A few years ago, one of my companies took a hit. I wrote down a list of seventeen things that I needed to do to fix it. I focused on them one by one. It took me about a year to get it done, but I did it. Those boards allow me to visually organize and, with clarity, take action. Those boards also help me compete against the things written on the board that I need to get done. I like to compete. My organizational system fuels my vehemence.

VIGOR

If you love what you do, that creates energy and vigor. In social media, young people call Sunday "Fun Day" and Wednesday "Hump Day"—like, oh boy! We are halfway through the week. My philosophy is this: Monday is Fun Day.

I enjoy my weekend with my family, but I can't wait for Monday to come. Monday is my chance to compete. I'm not competing over the weekend when I'm dining with my wife. I'm not competing when I hold my grandchildren in my arms and I'm hugging and kissing them. I'm not competing with my children when we are together. Monday morning comes and it's like, "Let me out!" And I can't wait to go. Vigor comes from really loving what you do.

VERACITY

I am very direct and I know what is going on in all my businesses. I walk the floor. I'm always interacting with employees. I am hands-on and face-to-face. I communicate very clearly and very directly what my expectations are. I also discuss with my team strategies for getting things done.

To work for me, you have to be thick-skinned. I am not mean, but I am very direct with my people. Humor is a tool. If one of my sales people is wasting time staring at a screen, I will tell them, "Stop staring at the computer system. Pick up the phone and make a call. Talk to your customers." I encourage my people to stay in the moment.

VICTORY

I know how to grow businesses. I've proven that, but I have learned to enjoy the journey as much as the destination.

My attitude is you never have to lose, so attack everything with an expectation of winning. Don't make excuses. Believe you're going to win every time. Play to that standard. Does that mean you're always going to win? No. But do everything in your power to win.

Recently, poet and singer Raegan Sealy debuted her poem "Champions" for an enthusiastic Philadelphia Soul crowd. The poem is a celebration of life and brings awareness to the champions around us—police officers, firefighters, teachers, and social service volunteers. One of the lines is, "There is a clock on this game—on time. / There is an end in sight, the finish line..."

There is a timeline on goals; staying in the moment helps us achieve those goals.

To stay current with Cosmo and his many entrepreneurial and humanitarian projects, visit cosmodenicola.com. To learn more about the causes close to Cosmo's heart, check out the "Cosmo Cares" page.

Bo Eason

"Even when I had injuries that required surgery, even when I was told I was no good, there was still no other option. This is going to happen. As soon as you give yourself an out, you are going to take it."

BO'S VICTORIES

Bo Eason started his five-year career in the NFL as the top pick for the Houston Oilers. He played for the San Francisco 49ers, competing beside and against some of the greatest players of his generation. In 2001, Bo wrote and performed his one-man play, *Runt of the Litter*, which opened in New York City to rave reviews. It is now being adapted as a major motion picture.

Bo helps others tap the power of their personal story and become effective and persuasive communicators through keynote speeches and workshops for major corporations. He has appeared as a guest on Fox Sports Net, ESPN, *The Rosie O'Donnell Show*, CNN, and *Real Time with Bill Maher*.

THE LAST LAUGH

I was just a kid, nine years old, when I wrote out my first dream or plan. I wrote it on that brown handwriting paper we used in school. That piece of paper is now forty-seven years old, falling apart like the Declaration of Independence. When I give speeches, I show it to the audience.

On that paper, I drew myself in a football uniform, surrounded by a bunch of players. The simple picture reflected my goal to be the best safety in the world. (A safety is a defensive back who lines up about 10-15 yards from the line of scrimmage and guards downfield passers.) I didn't want to just be a safety. I wanted to be the best safety in the world. That was the plan.

My brother was a quarterback. He was tall and stoic. I was really small. Many people laughed at my aspiration to be a football player. They thought it was cute. But I remained committed to my plan. I would wake up early in the morning and work on what safeties work on—running backwards.

I had an opportunity to play football in high school alongside my brother. We were a little farm school. Despite the fact we were undefeated, no college offered us scholarships. My brother went to a community college. I wasn't going to settle for that. I decided to go to UC Davis, a Division II school. There was no hope of a scholarship, but I was determined to play.

I walked on to practice, but after seeing me play, the coaches sent me home—too small and not good enough. My dream of being the best safety in the world was fading fast. I was told, "You can go to school here, but you're not going to play football."

What would I tell my parents? At this point, I made one of the smartest decision ever. I didn't leave. I had ten bucks to my name. I bought a big jar of peanut butter and two bags of stale hotdog buns so I would have something to eat. I slept in my 1977 Ford Courier pickup truck. I would go back to practice each day and each day they laughed at me.

The equipment guys were mean as hell—old Navy vets, tattooed up before tattoos were cool. They hated freshmen, especially me, who weighed 145 pounds soaking wet, but they found my determination amusing. They gave me a practice uniform. One problem: the uniform didn't match the rest of the team's. They also gave me a helmet. It was a relic. It was like Jim Thorpe had worn it. It was an old suspension helmet with a rope on the inside. No padding, just the canvas and rope. I would be humiliated and wouldn't show up anymore, they thought.

They were wrong. I kept showing up. There I was, sporting a mismatched uniform with an oversized helmet that bobbled up and down when I ran. The other players ignored me. Every now and then I would see the head coach tapping another coach on the shoulder and pointing. I'm sure he was saying, "Why is that freshmen still here in the goofy uniform? Didn't we send him home?"

Every night I would go back to my truck to eat those hot dog buns slathered in peanut butter and sleep. The next morning, I would go back to practice. Thirty days went by. Now it's time for our first game.

I show up in the locker room as if I'm going to play the game. I'm told by the equipment guys, "Hey, kid, you are not going to play. You are not even on the team. We were joking with you when we gave you that uniform. We thought it was cute."

I showed them my plan. "I've got a dream to be the best safety in the world, and I only have a few more years to do that. My mom and dad are going to be out there. They drove three hours to see me play. I just need to show up. I just need the opportunity."

That convinced them. They gave me a uniform. Again, it did not match the team. They instructed me to sit at a specific spot on the bench. The team had a hundred guys all suited up. I had to blend in. If the coach noticed me, the equipment guys could lose their jobs.

So, there I sat. I waved to my mom and dad up in the crowd. They were so excited. They actually thought I was on the team.

During that game, we were kicking butt. The score was 35–0. I'm scheming a way to get into the game. It was our turn to kick the ball deep. One of our best players, the captain of the team, was on the kickoff team. They had given us duplicate numbers. So here I am with a different uniform but the same number as our best player.

I pleaded with this guy to let me run down with the kickoff team. "Hey, man, my family is out there. They came all this way to see me play and they will be so disappointed if I don't get into this game. Just let me run down with the kickoff team for you."

His response: "You are crazy. The coaches are going to kill me."

I reminded him, "The coaches can't kill you. You are one of our best players." He agreed and let me run down.

I ran full speed. I was the first one on the field. This meant I was facing the wedge. My job would be to bust it. I was so small and these guys were so damn big—around 275 pounds each. Back in those days, it was legal for them to interlock arms. As they advanced toward me, I closed my eyes and dove over them. When I came down, to my surprise, I smacked the ball carrier and he went down in a heap.

The whole crowd rose to their feet, screaming. And I was screaming too. I ran off the field trying to be invisible because I knew the coaches saw that. I knew this was going to be the end of me. I knew the equipment guys were going to be in big trouble. I made myself as small as I could until the game was over.

After the game, I ran into the locker room and took off that uniform. I didn't even take a shower. I jumped into my civilian clothes and ran out to the truck. I ate yet another peanut butter and hot dog bun sandwich. I worried all weekend about what was going to come down.

I returned to practice on Monday morning. I was not sure what I would be facing, but I was determined to show up anyway. When I opened my locker, there was a brand-new varsity uniform.

Fast-forward four years. I was one of the top safeties chosen in the NFL draft.

Knee injuries eventually ended my football career. I still had this TNT inside of me, but I couldn't do what I did as a football player to release it. That would be illegal. I decided a safe and legal way to release that TNT was from the stage. I would be an actor.

At age twenty-nine, my dream changed from being the best safety in the world to being the best actor in the world. I moved to New York City to study theater. I didn't want to act in movies. I just wanted to act on stage. I had no idea what I was doing, but I realized I would have to start at the bottom again. I took classes in improvisation, movement, singing, acting, and writing. I channeled all the energy I used to become a great safety into becoming a great actor. I was a rookie and ten years older than the other students.

I asked my younger fellow classmates to identify the best stage performer of our time. This was the nineties. Every kid had the same answer—Al Pacino. I thought, "Okay, I am going to seek Al out and talk to him." Of course, I was laughed at again. By now I was used to that.

I called my agent from football and I said, "Hey, man. I need to meet this guy Al Pacino. Can you get us together?"

About three days later my agent got back to me. "I arranged a meeting with Al Pacino. A car is going to pick you up and take you to his house."

It was Thanksgiving and it was snowing. We made our way from Manhattan, across George Washington Bridge, to Al's house. He ran out to welcome me. He was much smaller than I had imagined. He was like, "Hey, Bo. Al Pacino."

I'm like, "No shit. You're the Godfather."

His house was filled with family making pasta and talking in Italian. It was like a scene from *The Godfather* or *Goodfellas*. He was enjoying the holiday with family before leaving the next day to work on the film *Frankie and Johnny* with Michelle Pfeiffer. While his family prepared the meal, we played pool. I relayed my request: "Everybody in my acting classes tells me you're the best actor around. I would like to have that mantle."

He was very humble, but forewarned me, "Yeah, well, I'm okay.

But to break that down, it's like fifteen years of stage work." I assured him that I work great in those timelines. The bottom line was: "If you really want this, you are going to have to have your butt on stage every chance you can, more than any other human being for the next fifteen to twenty years."

No problem. That is exactly what I did when I was a safety. I just ran backwards more than anyone else. He directed me to the best people with whom to study.

I committed all the money I made in football to getting the training I needed. After fifteen years, I got good, but I wasn't getting any great roles. I decided to write my own play and give myself the leading role. Again, people laughed. Football players aren't playwrights, after all. Write a play? I can't even spell that good. It took two years to complete *Runt of the Litter*, a semi-autobiographical account of my life and career as a safety.

We opened in New York City. The critics came out, no doubt expecting a disaster. "Football player turned playwright? Sure." After seeing the play, they changed their minds. *The New York Times* called it "one of the most powerful plays of the last decade." *Newsday* described it as "the kind of raw power rarely seen on stage." On her talk show, Rosie O'Donnell said, "Amazingly great. I loved it." We toured over fifty cities. We did that play 1,500 times.

Fifteen years after meeting Al Pacino, I was performing in New York. In the audience were celebrities, guys I used to envy because they were getting all the best roles—Tom Cruise, James Franco, Leonardo DiCaprio, and Toby McGuire. Castle Rock bought the rights to the movie. Frank Darabont is slated to write the screenplay. Darabont is a brilliant writer and director. He wrote *The Shawshank Redemption* and *The Green Mile* and has been nominated for three Academy Awards and a Golden Globe. Those celebrities were there because they wanted to play me.

Five rows back, in an aisle seat that night, was Al Pacino. We made eye contact. He gave me a slight nod like military guys do, like football players do. The nod of acknowledgement and respect.

That play led to my third career incarnation.

After the play, CEOs from major corporations—titans of industry—

would come backstage to meet me and my wife, Dawn. They were all requesting the same thing: "We want you to perform this at our next conference." That surprised me. I would always decline.

Then, one evening backstage, the CEO of a major insurance company approached me. Again, we declined. "No, we don't do that." To which he replied, "Well, that's too bad. We would fly your family to Hawaii for a five-star vacation and pay you..." When he told me how much, my jaw dropped. The speaker fee was ten times what I could make in theater. We were in.

Through the years, I have been told you are too small to play pro ball, you are not good looking enough or you are not tall enough to be a leading man. You? Write a play? No way. The opinions of others do not stop me. I continue to accomplish everything I set out to do, and it all started with that simple plan I wrote down at nine years old.

VISION

People can be so shortsighted. I learned a profound truth from a doctor who was a co-speaker at an event I was doing. "The people who are successful are the ones who have the most intimate and profound relationship with their future self." That made so much sense. He shared information about a company that had created a mirror that would age you twenty years. Every time you looked in the mirror, you saw yourself twenty years down the road. It was a tool that could help cultivate intimacy with your future self. I am now fifty-six, but I always project twenty years in the future. I ask myself, "What are you meant to be at seventy-six?" I practice those things now. I love those kinds of timelines.

VITALITY

Maintaining vitality also requires looking twenty years down the road. The question for me is, "Will I have the stamina/energy to fulfill my next dream twenty years from now? What will my relationship with my wife be like? What will my body look like? How will I feel?" I identify what I need to eat, drink, and do to fulfill the vision I have of myself at seventy-six. I make those adjustments today so I can have the vitality to fulfill my goals then.

VALOR

People look at my persistence to get on the team for UC Davis and consider me courageous. The truth is I was naïve and a little bit dumb. But it looked like courage. To keep showing up to practice was the only option I had.

In today's world, there are too many options. There is also the mentality that if this doesn't work, you have lots of other options. That leads to not mastering anything.

The elite performers I've met—the most sought-after speakers, lawyers, doctors, and others at the top of their game—got there because there was no option. They were going to do this. The fewer options you allow yourself, the braver you become. You get courageous.

My brother and I, from the time we were kids, had dreams of being pro football players. We had never met one. We didn't even really know what it took. Yet we were determined to be pro football players.

Friends of my parents tried to dissuade us. They counseled my parents to talk us out of that dream. They would say things like, "You better not put all their eggs in one basket," and, "You need a fallback plan, a plan B, otherwise they will face heartache and disappointment."

I remember my mom and dad asking those people to leave the house. They knew their intentions were good, but it was bad advice. Those friends were trying to be helpful and save us from disappointment and heartache. My parents were not interested in saving us from heartache. They were interested in option A, not option B. They were interested in all the eggs in one basket.

A doctor told me after a knee surgery, "You're done. You should never play again." My dad said, "The doctor is wrong. We've got a chance at this thing still." Even when I had injuries that required surgery, even when I was told I was no good, there was still no other option. This is going to happen. As soon as you give yourself an out, you are going to take it.

VEHEMENCE

My favorite definition for the word magnetism is this: "He or she has the power to affect others with the delight he or she takes in him or herself."

Larry Moss trained me in acting. He also directed my play, *Runt of the Litter*. He is an amazing guy. He understands audiences. He understands what they need and what they don't need. Most people look at their audience or their constituency and adjust to suit them. Larry taught me to ask, "What do you, the performer, need?" Not, "What does your audience want to see?" Ask, "What play do you want to see, Bo? What do you want to say?"

As long as you love your story, your audience will fall in love with the story too. They will be passionate about you the more you're passionate about you. When you are happy, your audience is happy. When you are passionate, your audience is passionate. It goes back to that magnetism quote: "He or she has the power to affect others with the delight he or she takes in him or herself."

VIGOR

My dream written down on a piece of paper has always righted my ship. My kids are doing this now. They're writing down their twenty-year dreams. Yes, big monster dreams attract naysayers. You will have well-meaning friends who tell you you're crazy. I remind my kids to look at that dream and right their ship. Let it take precedence over what anybody says.

It's like this: if we left Los Angeles and flew to Maui and we put that plane on automatic pilot, it would be off course 99% of the time, but it would continually adjust along the way. By the time we get to Maui, we would land within an inch of the intended destination. Autopilot is merely a self-righting mechanism.

If you think of your dreams and your plan as the destination, head in that direction and right the ship along the way. You gotta be okay with being off course 99% of the time. Most people aren't okay with that. They're ashamed of it. I'm not ashamed of it. I know it's part of the game.

Think of it like this: your plan is to lose ten pounds, and you go out and have a pizza, followed by a piece of cheesecake. Are you going to give up on your goal of losing ten pounds or are you going to get back on track? Too many people will quit right then and say, "I am so ashamed of myself. I made this commitment and now look at me." They will give up and go get another pizza. Not me. I let my plan, my dream, get me back on track.

VERACITY

Do what you say you're going to do. When I match what comes out of my mouth with what I do in the real world, the more integrity I have. The more integrity I have, the more quickly things will come into existence.

The better I got at matching my word to my action, the faster things happened. You can't speak your goals into existence if you're saying one thing and doing another. For example, if you say, "I will show up at the track tomorrow at 5 a.m.," and you don't, your body stops trusting what comes out of your mouth. But if you say, "I will be at the track at 5 a.m.," and you do it consistently, your body responds. I know what comes out of your mouth will happen. Your body will begin to line up with that integrity.

I call it matching the cuff with your collar. When you do that, things will begin to happen. You create intention. "I'm thirsty. My body needs hydration. I'm going to get a glass of water." And you do. That's where it begins. The more times I take action on my word, the more efficiently I can call things into existence. Over time I can say, "My body needs hydration..." and it hydrates based on intent. I know that sounds crazy. I was trained to have intention like that—to do exactly what I said I would do.

How many people do you know who cannot keep their word? It's not that they're bad people, it's just that they cannot keep their word. Their body doesn't match up with what comes out of their mouth. Sadly, most of the world lives there. They say one thing and do another.

VICTORY

I remember when Michael Jordan was winning those six championships for the Bulls in the nineties. He would put his arms above his head in celebration briefly and then his hands would drop. You could see it on his face that the celebration was now over. He was on to next year.

In the NFL, every win is short-lived. The highest achievers don't celebrate that long. They raise their hands in celebration, they hug their teammates and then the next question is, "How do we do this again? Next game? Next year?"

Interested in learning more about Bo and how he trains people to use their personal stories to create more impact in their careers and businesses? Go to boeason.com and join his mailing list.

Jim Harbaugh

"You need to set your dreams and goals so high that everybody laughs at them. If nobody is laughing at your dreams and goals, you haven't set them high enough."

JIM'S VICTORIES

Jim is the head coach for the University of Michigan Wolverines. He is a former college quarterback and played for Michigan under the legendary head coach Glenn "Bo" Schembechler from 1983–86.

Jim played quarterback in the NFL for fourteen seasons with the Chicago Bears, Indianapolis Colts, Baltimore Ravens, and the San Diego Chargers. He was honored as the NFL Comeback Player of the Year in 1995 for the Indianapolis Colts.

Over the course of his career as a coach, he has served as a quarterback coach for the Oakland Raiders, head coach for the University of San Diego and Stanford University for The Cardinal (where he lead the team to the 2011 Orange Bowl), and head coach for the San Francisco 49ers, whom he led to three NFC Championships and ultimately to Super Bowl XLVII.

He is the son of coach Jack Harbaugh and the brother of world champion NFL coach John Harbaugh of the Baltimore Ravens.

THE LAST LAUGH

We moved to Michigan when I was nine. My favorite thing to do was play sports. My second favorite thing was to be around the Michigan football team, going to practices and watching the older guys, the college guys, that I looked up to so much.

In eighth grade, I attended a University of Michigan football camp. There were mainly high schoolers there. I was able to go to the camp because my dad was a coach at Michigan. They separated us by grade, tenth through twelfth. I went with the tenth grade quarterbacks.

There was a coach there who wasn't on the Michigan staff at that time but who eventually became an NFL quarterback coach. He told me that I didn't have a strong enough arm to play quarterback. He said that I should play a different position like safety or corner. He said I was pretty athletic, but he didn't think that I was strong enough to be a quarterback. So I told him, "Hey, coach. I'm only in the eighth grade." I do laugh about that. I ended up playing professional football as an NFL quarterback for fourteen years.

Within a month of leaving the NFL as a player, I was hired by the great Al Davis, the principal owner and manager of the Oakland Raiders, to be a quality control coach (the guy who helps prepare the team by analyzing game footage and play statistics and keeps all business and player systems current).

That is really the lowest man on the totem pole. A year later, I was still the lowest man on the totem pole in quality control, but they also promoted me to quarterback coach.

After year two, I had an opportunity to be the head coach at the University of San Diego. I went to Mr. Davis and told him. He responded, "I thought you wanted to be a pro coach. I thought that was why you were here. That's why I hired you."

And I said, "Well, Mr. Davis. I studied your career and noticed that you started as a college coach. I want to emulate your career and follow in your footsteps and become a head coach."

Mr. Davis said, "Yeah, Jim, but that was USC (University of Southern California) not USD (University of San Diego, a member of the NCAA Pioneer Football League)."

That made some sense. There had never been, in the history of the Pioneer Football League, a head coach who had advanced to a head coach position in the professional ranks of the NFL. Since that time, there have been several. But I felt like that was the right thing for me to do at that time.

Nine years after accepting that position at USD, a college that does not even offer football scholarships, I was headed to the Super Bowl as head coach of the San Francisco 49ers to play the Baltimore Ravens, a team coached by my brother, John Harbaugh.

VISION

Vision is a three-part thing.

1. Have a vision. Vision is the beginning. You need a clear vision of where you want to go with the organization you're involved with. You need to be able to clearly communicate that to everybody around you.

2. Have a plan. That plan needs to be executable and simple. It should be easy to remember.

3. Have the patience to carry out that plan. I call it patience, but some people call it stubbornness. You need it to execute your plan in the face of naysayers and the many people surrounding you who tell you how you can do things better.

You need to set your dreams and goals so high that everybody laughs at them. If nobody is laughing at your dreams and goals, you haven't set them high enough.

VITALITY

It's important to find a balance of eating right, getting exercise, and taking care of yourself.

I stay within my priorities: faith, family, and football. I am married to a phenomenal woman, Sarah Harbaugh. I have seven great kids. I have a job that keeps me active. That keeps me pretty busy.

I don't consider stress a debilitator. Stress is life-giving energy.

I avoid the fun stuff. I don't go out and party and go to bars.

I eat when I'm hungry.

I don't have a specific regimen. I believe in being a jackhammer. Keep going. I just keep going. That seems to be working well for me.

VALOR

Atticus, in the book *To Kill a Mockingbird*, said, "[Courage] is when you know you're licked before you begin but you begin anyway and you see it through no matter what."

Doing something when the odds are against you takes courage. Most of the time, you don't prevail. But every now and then, you do. That's the way I look at it. I have had a lot of success with doing things even when I don't start out with the courage to do them. I do them anyway and get the courage later.

On the field, I transform fear into aggression. It works out better than being scared of something. Sometimes you do get whipped. Sometimes you do lose, but every once in a while, you don't.

Live in a state of grace. Put your trust in the Lord and be not afraid.

VEHEMENCE

Ralph Waldo Emerson said, "Nothing great was ever achieved without enthusiasm."

Jack Harbaugh, my father, said, "Attack each day with enthusiasm unknown to mankind." There you go. Two of the world's great philosophers agree, so it must be right.

VIGOR

A strong mindset starts with a vision—a grand vision that is clearly communicated. The people that you have on your team are very important. You need to surround yourself with people who have integrity and skill and who are willing to work and give their best effort. You need people who believe and share the same vision and agree to the direction.

You must get the right people on your team—motivated people. Teammates that are inspired. It is very hard to motivate the unmotivated.

Create a "meritocracy" where promotions will be predicated on merit. By their talent and efforts, they will be known. There should be no politics or playing favorites. There should be fair, healthy, and honest competition. Each person should be recognized for their effort and their talent. Everybody deserves the guarantee of an opportunity based on what they can produce.

I reinforce that message all the way through. Known expectations produce strength of mind.

VERACITY

I trust a liar about as much as I trust a rattlesnake. I believe in truth. I believe that all the mind games, motivational tricks, and gimmicks have been tried. The honest truth is a powerful motivator in itself. No lying. No stealing. No cheating. I reinforce that with my team and in my life every chance I get.

VICTORY

My very favorite word in the English language is victory. The second is homecoming, the third is family, the fourth is reckoning, the fifth is meritocracy, the sixth is stalwart. But victory is the favorite of all my favorite words.

Victory with a team is the most wonderful feeling that I know. Whether it is a football team, your family team, or the country team, the United States of America. When you accomplish something as a team, the feeling is magnified exponentially. There's no greater joy or feeling than to be part of a team victory. Small or large.

Victory is the result of ongoing improvement. Be better today than you were yesterday. Be better tomorrow than you were today. That's a plan for success. It's so simple. It might just work.

In football, it's not fun when you lose. That's a heartbreaking thing. But there's a new week and a new opportunity. I definitely get happier and happier as that new opportunity approaches. So, "win the next game." That's my mindset.

To enjoy more of Jim Harbaughs wisdom, order his books, Enthusiasm Unknown to Mankind *and* Rise Again *at enthusiasmunknowntomankind.com.*

Mariel Hemingway

"Until you understand your past, you cannot stay focused in the present. Our homework as human beings is to excavate our past, to look deeply into the things that make us who we are now. Your moment-by-moment focus will be continually interrupted by the nagging voices of the past if you don't do your homework."

MARIEL'S VICTORIES

Mariel Hemingway is an iconic Academy Award-nominated actress from a celebrated family. She is a prolific author and an entrepreneur and a sought-after speaker focused on mind-body-spirit optimization and purposeful living. She has been profiled in or appeared on several national media outlets, including *USA Today*, *The Chicago Tribune*, *Today*, *Vanity Fair*, *The New York Times*, and *People*.

Mariel has appeared in movie and television hits like *Manhattan*, *Lipstick*, *Personal Best*, *Star 80*, *Superman IV: The Quest for Peace*, and *Papa* (2016). In 2014, *Running from Crazy*, a rich and evocative award-winning and Emmy-nominated documentary about the Hemingway family, which Mariel co-executive produced with Oprah Winfrey, premiered at the Sundance Film Festival. It documents her boundless advocacy for mental health awareness, the dignity and rights of people of all circumstance and ability, and her commitment to connecting those of like mind and heart in order to optimize their lives in the best and worst of times.

THE LAST LAUGH

I was an awkward kid, gangly and insecure. My childhood was lonely. I was bullied at school by peers and at home by my older siblings, who viewed me as competition for our parents' attention. At eleven years old, I became caretaker for my mother, who was diagnosed with cancer. I had to be the parent. My insecurities and responsibilities kept me isolated.

Being the granddaughter of iconic author Ernest Hemingway opened some doors for me, but there was also a very dark side. With that Hemingway history came the DNA of mental illness and addiction. Seven of my family members committed suicide, including my grandfather and my sister, Margaux. I believe my grandfather, who shot himself in 1961, four months before I was born, suffered from undiagnosed bipolar disorder.

I grew up watching a family that was completely amazing and creative but also destructive and self-medicating. I lived with the gnawing fear that I would be next. I would become crazy or I would commit suicide. I didn't want to end up like that.

Instead of allowing myself to be consumed by that fear, I channeled it into becoming a mental health advocate. I produced a documentary called *Running from Crazy*. It was nominated for an Emmy Award for Outstanding Documentary in 2014. I also wrote two books on the subject, *Out Came the Sun: Overcoming the Legacy of Mental Illness, Addiction, and Suicide in My Family* and *Invisible Girl*, written diary-style and aimed at teenagers. Telling my story has been liberating. It is one of my last laughs.

Becoming an actress is also a last laugh for me. I was a shy and insecure little girl, not on track to become a successful actress—but it happened.

I remember when film legend Woody Allen called our house to discuss casting me as the co-star in *Manhattan*. I was just a kid, outside jumping on a trampoline. My mom called me and was obviously very excited that THE Woody Allen wanted to talk with me. I had no clue who this guy was at the time. My starring role in *Manhattan* led to me being nominated for an Academy Award and travelling to Cannes. Suddenly, my little world enlarged. Instead of being invisible and dismissed, people were seeking me out and listening to what I had to say.

My last laughs are not about laughing at others but laughing at the fears that could have kept me in bondage but ultimately did not. I came out of isolation and insecurity to create the glorious life I now live.

Even more significant than the things I have done are the lessons I have learned along the way. I spent many years seeking out the teacher or guru who could tell me what to do. I now know I am the expert on ME. Yes, I learn from others, but I am the expert on how I should live my life.

VISION

Though I am always engaged in a project, I am not a person who projects ten years down the road. My vision is more present. If I become clear and honest about who I am now and I maintain balance in my life, I discover the path to the next project. Vision for me is more of a day to day unveiling, here and now, than a dream of something down the road.

VITALITY

There are three things that most people do not get enough of: breath, silence, and water. These are things that you have to mindfully make part of your life if you are to maintain your energy. They don't just happen.

- **Breath**—There are many techniques on how to breathe, but it all starts with making sure you are. I used to spend a lot of time holding my breath and I wasn't even aware of it. Now, each morning, I go through a very specific series of breathing exercises. This primes my energy for the day.

- **Silence**—Call it meditation. Call it prayer. Taking breaks to still our soul is so very important. My moment of silence starts in the morning as I watch the sun rise. This is my morning meditation. There is something so powerful about the cyclical nature of the rising and setting of the sun. I used to get hung up on perfecting how to practice silence. Don't worry about how long you spend or if you have intrusive thoughts. We are people. We think. Just stop and be silent. Even if it is just for five minutes. In silence, we find serenity and we also find answers.

- **Water**—Most of us are not drinking enough water. Ever wonder why people in humid climates have great skin? You guessed it—water. And water does the same thing when taken internally. It also can help us maintain our weight, our energy, and our vitality. Start each day with a tall, refreshing glass of water.

VALOR

It takes courage to confront your past. It requires digging deep into those sometimes-dark places. It also takes courage to reach beyond the past. Climbing rocks is a scary thing for me. It is a great metaphor for the process of achievement. You have to overcome your fear and be in the moment. When I climb rocks, sometimes I am scared. Sometimes I cry, but I keep going. When I complete the climb, I realize, yes, there were real dangers that I had to guard against, but much of the fear was not real. Those imaginary fears can keep us from making progress if we let them.

VEHEMENCE

I share a common passion with my grandfather. I love engaging with nature. Watching the sun rise and the sun set, smelling the air, touching the earth—these simple pleasures stoke my passion for living. Nature is where God speaks to me. It is more than a pastime. It is my religion.

To live a meaningful life, you need to discover your passion. Find that place, those people, and those activities that amplify your sense of purpose—that awaken and stoke your personal power.

VIGOR

Living with vigor requires focus. Until you understand your past, you cannot stay focused in the present. Our homework as human beings is to excavate our past, to look deeply into the things that make us who we are now. Your moment-by-moment focus will be continually interrupted by the nagging voices of the past if you don't do your homework.

Those voices of the past are not our voice. They are the voices of parents, teachers, and peers. They can be like rude guests that come to dinner. They don't say please or thank you. They interrupt you. They complain about the meal you made. They tell you what a horrible host you are. If they were guests, you would kick them out. Too often we let these guests take up residence in our head. To maintain your vigor, you need to acknowledge that these rude thoughts are not yours. Acknowledge their existence and kick them out. Welcome the voice of kindness and love that builds you up, not the voice that tears you down.

Once you have silenced the voices of the past, stay focused on the present. Sustain that focus through living a balanced life. One of my pastimes is walking a tight rope. If you lean too far in either direction, you will fall. It's the same thing in life. Avoid the extremes. Mindfully stay the course and you will have the vigor you need to accomplish what you need to accomplish.

Sometimes life can derail your balance. At those times, you really need to be able to stay focused on what is important. As a child, I was determined to stay true to my moral compass. It was not entirely healthy. It was more of a control thing. But it did keep me from falling into addiction and destructive living like some of my family members did. Now that I am older and wiser, staying mindful and balanced is a joyful dynamic, rather than an obsessive fear of making a mistake or letting someone down.

VERACITY

It took me a long time to learn to be true to myself. My biggest obstacle to living with veracity was I did not trust that I knew what was best for me. I grew up in a home that was out of control. I wanted everyone to be happy. I wanted everyone to love me. Being honest about who you are and what you believe opens you to rejection. I didn't want to be rejected so I didn't speak my mind. I was always looking to other people to tell me what I needed to do and affirm that I was doing the right thing. I didn't trust my own inner voice. I'm now older and wiser. I have learned to be honest with myself and with others about who I am and what I believe.

VICTORY

I've overcome the dark parts of the Hemingway legacy. I want my daughters to live their lives without the burden of thinking, "Oh, because there is mental illness in my family, I'm going to go crazy." I took responsibility to look hard at myself, deal with that legacy, and not pass it on to them. I now live a simple and beautiful life. I've learned to stand on my own two feet. I've learned to trust my inner voice. That's my victory.

To learn more about Mariel's many projects, visit her website: marielhemingway.com.

Helie Lee

"Deception is toxic. Truth is like water flushing out the toxins. Truth can be hurtful, but in the end it will compel you to make a change."

HELIE'S VICTORIES

Helie Lee is the author of two bestsellers. Her first book, *Still Life with Rice*, chronicles her family's experience in war-torn Korea from the 1930s to 1997. Her second book, *The Absence of Sun*, details her risky attempt to rescue her uncle from North Korea.

Helie also wrote and produced *Macho Like Me*, a one-woman show featuring a monologue juxtaposed with video footage that follows her experience living as a man for six months. *Macho Like Me* has since been adapted into a full-length documentary.

Helie has been featured on or in *Nightline*, CNN, *NBC Nightly News*, NPR, *The Los Angeles Times*, *Chicago Tribune*, *People*, *Life & Times*, *Today*, *Oprah*, and the Associated Press and has spoken as a guest lecturer at Stanford, Yale, Harvard, Princeton, Northeastern University, Amherst, the Korean American Coalition, and KASCON, among many other venues. Her work has been published in *Mademoiselle*, *Essence*, and *KoreAm Journal*.

In June of 2002, Lee was invited to testify at the Senate Subcommittee Hearing on Immigration. Lee is the co-founder of The Korea Academy for Educators (KAFE). She has served as a board member for the San Diego Asian American Film Festival and the U.S. Committee for Human Rights in North Korea.

THE LAST LAUGH

In my memoir, *The Absence of Sun*, I share the experience of rescuing my uncle and his family from North Korea. At the time, I was in a horrific relationship. I'm pretty sure a lot of women can identify with it. My boyfriend wanted me to forfeit my career, my dreams, my last name. He wanted me to do all his laundry and cook his meals. He wanted me to tie my identity to him and lose my sense of self.

If I stayed in that relationship, it would've been a pretty cushy life. He was very successful. I could have everything I wanted. But it wasn't worth selling my soul and my essence. It wasn't worth sacrificing my gifts and the gifts I had yet to discover.

It took courage to end that relationship. I was penniless at the time.

I didn't have a place to live. I fell into a deep depression. But I knew that was exactly where I was supposed to be.

While I was in that dark valley, my father asked me to join him on a mission to help rescue my uncle and family. I didn't even have to think about it. I was going. I had a choice: I could sit there and cry and go back to my relationship, or I could go through this door that had opened for me.

My friends thought I was insane. "You are not talking about China or Cuba or some other oppressive country; you're talking about North Korea, the most tyrannical regime in the world." But I knew this door had opened and my family needed me. I'm driven by loyalty and duty to my family. The deep love I have for them is because I have received love from them. I took a leap of blind faith and moved forward with my father.

There were times when it was very dangerous. It was like being surrounded by a storm, but I felt like I was in the eye of the storm, where it was calm.

The outcome? We rescued nine family members. There were a lot of different feelings. Feelings of vindication. "F*** you, North Korea." We did it! There was gratitude and tears. My grandmother, who had been suffering so many years, was reunited with her family.

This was quite a last laugh for a Valley girl. I grew up in the Valley totally protected. But I also grew up with the awareness that there are millions of North Koreans who are suffering, separated from their families. I knew I had a larger responsibility to shine a light on what is going on in North Korea. The love my parents showed me gave me the confidence and awareness I needed to pick up the pebbles that led to that open door.

After the rescue, I did a gender study. I lived as a man for six months. I cut my hair, changed my clothes, and moved out of my home to a place where nobody knew me as Helie Lee or as a female. The outcome was the documentary *Macho Like Me*.

For me to learn about something, I put myself in the other person's shoes (or their underwear and clothes). This gave me the closest and most authentic experience possible. I would never want to be a man. I learned that men have it so much harder than I ever gave them credit for. I am truly in awe and have tremendous respect for them. I think I needed to go through that experience to see how the other side lived.

Again, people were like, "You can't do that." My thought was, "Hey, I helped rescue nine people from North Korea. Why can't I be a man for a few months?" All my life I have had people tell me I can't do something. Once someone tells me I can't, that inspires me to break through that wall and prove that I can.

With any challenge in life, if you can laugh a little bit, it puts everything in perspective. It lifts the burden, the drama, the guilt, the hurt. Laughter is the best medicine. In the darkest moments, you can always find a reason to laugh.

VISION

I envision outcomes. I see myself in any situation at the finish line. I see myself getting an Oscar. I see my children growing up and receiving a humanitarian award as a result of my work with them. I see my parents living to 100, sitting in my living room with their great-grandchildren at their knees. I don't see the journey. I see the moment when I have achieved what I want to achieve.

Visualization also helps me maintain my passion. If I have a problem that needs to be resolved, I ask myself, "How am I going to end the story? How am I going to solve this problem? What are the right words that I need to make this right?" I sleep on it and let my subconscious go where it needs to go, the heavens or wherever. In the morning, I always have an answer.

I also envision my many facets. I see myself as a many-armed woman wearing an apron and a chef hat and many other outfits. I have scissors in one hand and a computer in the other. I wear skates on one foot and running shoes on the others. I have the power to transform at will.

Korean women are like bamboo. They are strong. In the storm or through tragedy we bend but we never break. I am like bamboo. I am strong. I'm tall. I'm lean. I touch the sky, but my roots are deep. A great wind could blow me over, but I will never break. This bamboo-like quality allows people to lean on me for strength.

VITALITY

I've done modern dance all my life. I gravitate towards music and rhythm. I used to take classes and be very rigid about my exercise routine, but now I just dance. I love to flow in dance and do what I want. I'm at an age that I don't want people telling me what to do. I don't need to go to a Pilates class or a boot camp. I don't need somebody to push me. I have inner discipline. I know what my body can take or not take. I do what my body tells me to do. That comes with maturity and also having gone to hell and back.

VALOR

My life has been driven by both faith and fear.

There have been times in my life where I've been afraid. I was afraid to immigrate to this country. I was afraid to go to a school where nobody looked like me. I was afraid to date my first boyfriend. But a bigger fear is missing opportunities when doors open for me. That is what drives me.

So when I feel fear, I expect something great is on the other end. I bulldoze through the fear. I go for it.

Once I walk through a door, I am driven by faith. I don't think about the repercussions or the danger. I have the ultimate faith that I will get through to the other end. Whatever the journey I am on, I know that's exactly where I must be. The mistakes I make along the way are the mistakes I am supposed to make along the way. I don't consider mistakes to be failures. They are part of the learning process. They give me another step that will lead to the next step and the next.

It doesn't take any more courage to rescue people from North Korea than to walk into a new school for the first time. It's the same courage whether the challenge is big or small. I am courageous. I call it BAD ASS. I have the courage to pick up the pebbles on my path that lead to whatever door I am supposed to walk through.

Courage can be bad ass, but courage can also be gentle and speak softly. You have to be wise enough to know which to use when.

VEHEMENCE

I can! I will! I must! This is an affirmation I taught to my children and their friends. When my children have a challenging task to accomplish, I tell them, "Speak that affirmation and make your hands into fists and punch the air and scream, loud, 'I can! I will! I must!'" This affirmation creates energy and determination. When my kids are sleeping, I will whisper it in their ears, so it goes deep into their subconscious.

VIGOR

There are a lot of monsters around us trying to drain our creativity and take our attention away from our dreams, goals, and desires. I block them out. It's like I have headphones on. I sense when people are projecting their insecurities and heartache on me. I accept what is my responsibility and ignore what is not. It's their problem, not mine. This allows me to maintain the energy I need to move forward and assist my community and my family. I feel fortunate that I have the energy and means to serve others.

There are times I need to restore that energy because I have spread myself too thin. When I was an unmarried writer, I spent years secluded in my house by myself with a cup of coffee in my comfy slippers just writing and being creative.

Now I'm married and I have seven-year-old twins. Parents and friends come in and out of my house all day long. It can be very distracting and literally suck all the energy out of me. I have to take time—whether it's ten minutes or an hour—just to get by myself. One of my favorite places to sit is my closet. There, I have total peace. To recharge, I close my eyes, center, and breathe. I let whatever thoughts come to mind inspire me.

I also recharge in my car. I spend a lot of time there. I am a busy mom taking my kids around town. I have my coffee cup and my laptop and even a good book in my car. It is my cocoon and it feels safe. I even do meetings in my car. I love bringing people into my cocoon.

VERACITY

The truth can hurt, but in the end, it saves you ten times the pain. It is important for your spiritual and your personal growth to hear the truth.

Deception is toxic. Truth is like water flushing out the toxins. Truth can be hurtful, but in the end, it will compel you to make a change. It will compel you to take action.

North Korea is a society lacking truth. Where there is no truth, there is distrust. You distrust everyone, including your own family. When there is distrust, you cannot lean on each other. This has made North Korea a very fragile society.

In other communist countries, information from the outside can seep in. Not North Korea. It has been expertly sealed off. Their citizens are so afraid. If they are caught with a news magazine or a western movie, they are sent to a prison camp. The people are like frightened animals ready to lash out. South Korea and others are looking for ways to get truth into North Korea. Truth creates revolution.

VICTORY

I celebrate victories with gratitude. Without gratitude, there will be no success around the corner. I express gratitude to the people who helped me along in the journey.

I also express gratitude for the lessons learned. Sometimes I get the thing right the first time. Sometimes I make mistakes, but I don't beat myself up. I don't tell myself, "Helie, you're such a loser." I consider the mistake a lesson I needed to learn again. There a chance for growth if one can accept imperfection and truth.

For example, in the past, I might have dated the wrong guy. I end the relationship, but next time around, I am dating another guy with those same qualities. Is that a failure? No: sometimes that happens so you can learn the lesson you need to learn one more time. After making the same mistake again, the lessons become embedded in your DNA. They help you make better decisions down the road.

To learn more about Helie and her work and to purchase her books, visit helielee.com.

Colonel Tom Manion

"Every day we would wake up and affirm ourselves,
'If not me, then who...' This fueled the courage we
needed to face whatever challenges the day brought."

COLONEL MANION'S VICTORIES

Col. Tom Manion started his career in the Marine Corps, retiring after thirty years. Tom joined Johnson & Johnson in 1990 and through the years held various leadership roles before retiring in 2014. Tom is the father of 1st Lt. Travis Manion, a Marine leader who made the ultimate sacrifice for our country in April of 2007. After the loss of Travis, the family established the Travis Manion Foundation (TMF) to support our military, the families of the fallen, and to help create the next generation of leaders. Through the foundation, Tom has worked within the community and around the country to inspire people around him to convey a sense of sacrifice and public service in all they do. Tom's late wife Janet Manion, founder and visionary of the Travis Manion Foundation, passed away April 24, 2012. She was known for devoting every day to putting service above self. Tom is also the co-author of the recently released book, *Brothers Forever*, the story of friendship, service, and sacrifice of Travis and his Naval Academy roommate Lt. (SEAL) Brendan Looney.

THE LAST LAUGH

In 2007, our son Travis, a Marine, was killed by a sniper in Fallujah, Iraq. His best friend and roommate at the Naval Academy, Brendan Looney, a Navy SEAL, died in a tragic helicopter crash almost four years later. These two young men have come to define a new generation who didn't hesitate in the aftermath of 9/11 to put themselves in harm's way in service to their country. They paid the ultimate sacrifice and are now buried side-by-side in Arlington's National Cemetery.

Before Travis's final deployment to Iraq, he shared something that has become a core value for us and so many in the country. He and my son-in-law, Dave, went to an Eagles game together. It was the playoffs and the Eagles won. We are die-hard Eagles fans, so they were feeling pretty good. While leaving the game, Dave, who was worried about Travis's return to Iraq, kiddingly said, "Hey Travis. I could trip you down the stairs, then you wouldn't have to go back to Iraq."

Travis got quiet and very serious. He turned to Dave and said, "You know what though, Dave? I'm the one who is ready to go. If I don't go, then someone much less prepared will have to go in my place. If not me, then who..." Those words have fueled all our efforts. They are etched on Travis' grave marker in Arlington for eternity.

Shortly after losing Travis, Janet and I established the Travis Manion Foundation (TMF). We decided the foundation would be there to support our veterans and the families of the fallen, and would also play a part in creating the next generation of leaders.

My last conversation with Travis when he was in Iraq was difficult because of a poor connection. We kept getting cut off, but the one thing he repeated to me, the message he wanted me to have, was that there was a big difference between what he was seeing in the news and what was happening around him in Fallujah. Despite the bad connection, the message from Travis was loud and clear. Awareness of and true appreciation for the sacrifice, selfless service, love of country, and heroism of our service men and women needs to be more visible and real for the rest of the country.

So, when the Marine knocked on our door to deliver the message that we had lost our son, we wanted to shut the door and close the windows and grieve. We knew there was going to be a lot of media attention. I couldn't forget Travis's last message to me. As hard as it was, we had to face that attention so we could share that message. If not me, then who, right? Every time we faced the media, we felt compelled to share Travis' story and the story of his brothers and sisters in uniform.

The foundation continues the work of sharing that message. Travis's sister, Ryan, now serves as president, and Brendan's widow, Amy, serves as vice president. The movement continues to grow.

A centerpiece of the effort is connecting veterans who have served to our nation's youth, some of whom have never had a positive role model or a mentor. The TMF ambassadors share stories of real people who exemplify great character and leadership. They demonstrate what it means to live the "If not me, then who..." ethos. They provide mentorship to help students foster the character they need to have a positive impact on the nation, whether they ever serve in uniform or not.

In another effort to build awareness, each year on or near September 11th, local volunteers who have asked themselves "If not me, then who..."

organize 9/11 Heroes Runs on behalf of TMF in more than sixty cities around the world. Thousands of runners and walkers of all levels and all ages come together to recognize those heroes that we've lost since 9/11 and those in uniform that continue to serve their communities and country.

So, out of Travis's loss, the Travis Manion Foundation was formed, and the "If not me, then who..." movement was started. In 2014, I co-authored a book, *Brothers Forever*. The book is not just about Travis and Brendan. Through their story, it tells the bigger story of all the brothers and sisters who have served so bravely and proudly for our country. It's about all the heroes that made the ultimate sacrifice and continue to inspire us as a nation.

VISION

In the early days, raw emotion and passion drove us. But you need more than raw emotion and passion. You need preparation and a plan to establish a vision. This is how it worked for us.

We would get up every day and affirm, "If not me, then who..." That would give us the motivation we needed to attack the day.

We had to do our research, meet the right people, and create an action plan for the foundation and other things we were doing.

It was easy to get overwhelmed by all the opportunities we were faced with, but we realized we could not be all things to all people. We had to focus on what was important to the mission and stick with it.

It was hard work, but we had a vision to spread a positive message to, about, and for our men and women in uniform in every way we could. We spread it through the activities of the foundation.

VALOR

After such a life-changing loss, there was nothing that we were going to back away from. We were willing to take on anything and anyone. It took courage to face the media, to launch the foundation, and to write a book. Every day we would wake up and affirm, "If not me, then who..." This fueled the courage we needed to face whatever challenges the day brought.

Travis taught us a lot about courage, not just on the battlefield, but in everyday life. After his loss, we learned from so many friends how he consistently lived out the "If not me, then who..." approach to life. Like Travis, Brendan Looney also epitomized that spirit.

VIGOR

We had a lot of support for what we were doing, but there were some who couldn't visualize us as anything more than a small family foundation. This made us question whether we could realistically make this happen, but we were determined to push through the self-doubt. We kept focused on the positive and kept our eye on the goal.

Along the way of building the foundation, we would have signs that Travis was with us. This motivated us to keep going, knowing we were on the right track. My faith helps me, and I truly believe that Travis, Janet, and I will see each other again. In the meantime, there is work to do here on Earth.

VERACITY

I am honest to a fault sometimes. That's how I am. Being straight up is important. I believe in being true to yourself, true to others, and true to God. I have committed myself to spreading the message about our military and those that serve others, our communities, and our country. I want people to appreciate our great country and those who protect us and our freedoms. Travis fought and died so that we would have the freedom to express our opinion.

VITALITY

If I didn't stay fit and eat right, I would not be here. One thing I do regularly is run. Running brings down my stress. It clears my mind and helps me focus. Some of my best ideas come when I am running. Consistency is the key. Whatever exercise you choose, make it part of your daily routine.

Don't forget about how important a healthy diet is to your overall well-being. In the past, starchy and sugary carbs were a big part of my diet. I have moved more toward lean protein, greens, and non-starchy vegetables. It has helped me keep my energy levels in check and to maintain a healthy weight.

VEHEMENCE

One thing that helps me keep the flame lit is realizing how important our mission is. The first few years, I had passion like you wouldn't believe. It has been ten years now, and it does get harder to feel the same energy.

Something that fuels my vehemence is sharing Travis and Brendan's story and the stories of other great Americans who have made sacrifices for all of us. This helps me fulfill the mission that Travis gave me the last time I spoke with him—to tell their story. This also helps me to live out the "If not me, then who..." ethos. I am motivated by what we have accomplished thus far. We have a long way to go, but we have made such a great impact already.

VICTORY

We always celebrated our successes as a family. Family is what is most important to us. Now that Travis and Janet are gone, my daughter and I celebrate with a nod to one another, acknowledging when something has gone right. We don't spend a lot of time celebrating. We say, "That's great. What's next?" A lot has been done. There is a lot more to do.

You can learn more about the Travis Manion Foundation at travismanion.org. To purchase Brothers Forever, *go to amazon.com.*

Heather Mitts Feeley

"My encouragement to others is to use negativity to motivate you. There's this amazing quote, 'Tell me I can't and then watch me work twice as hard to prove you wrong.'"

HEATHER'S VICTORIES

Heather has played soccer for the University of Florida, Women's Professional Soccer (WPS), the Philadelphia Charge, the Boston Breakers, the Philadelphia Independence, and the Atlanta Bear. She is a three-time Olympic gold medalist and a former member of the U.S. Women's National Team, with whom she played four matches in the 2011 FIFA Women's World Cup.

As a broadcaster, Heather has served as a TV analyst and sideline reporter for ABC, ESPN, ESPN2, MLS, and the American College Football league. She was also featured as a swimsuit model on the cover of *Sports Illustrated* in 2006 and hosted her own reality show.

Heather and fellow Olympian Angela Hucles recently founded the Ceres Platinum Group, a company that works to connect retired athletes with each other and create meaningful careers after their sports careers have ended. Her other entrepreneurial ventures include running a soccer camp, in which she teaches the basics of soccer to young athletes, and the production of a series of workout and lifestyle videos titled "Empowered Pregnancy" with sports physiologist Shannon Grady. Heather and her husband, NFL Quarterback A.J. Feeley, have two children, Connor and Blake Harper.

THE LAST LAUGH

I grew up in an active family. We were always playing sports. My brother, Brian, was eighteen months younger than me. We started competing from a very young age in 1 v. 1 battles. He became really good at soccer at a very young age. That pushed me to want to do whatever he did. So we would have these showdowns in the backyard. These early years cultivated my competitive temperament.

I also learned by watching my dad. He taught me that if you want something badly enough, you can achieve it. He was a very successful cardiac surgeon and grew up on a farm in Kentucky. He had nothing. Despite the odds against him, he is now one of the most successful cardiac surgeons in Cincinnati.

I played a lot of different sports growing up. In my freshman year of high school, my mom asked me to focus on one sport. I chose soccer. She couldn't believe it because I was really good at tennis. She counseled me that soccer was not a sport you can play when you're older. I explained to her, "That doesn't matter to me. I love it."

Initially, my father didn't support my dream of playing soccer. He wanted me to focus on getting educated and finding a more sustainable pursuit. I did get a great education, but along the way, I did what I love: played soccer.

I didn't have a vision past playing in college. The pressure was on. I had a short amount of time to prove myself. I was determined to be the best that I could be. Instead of just doing the minimum of what my coaches expected, I sought to do over and above. I identified my weaknesses and focused on improving daily.

Then, one day, my coach asked me what my goals were. I shared my goals. They were not that lofty. I told him, "My goal is to be the best college player possible." He asked, "Why don't you set your sights on being on the Women's National Team?" I didn't think it was a possibility. He advised me to "plant that seed," explaining that success in soccer is a marathon and not a sprint. Right then and there I manifested that I wanted to be on the Women's National Soccer Team.

Most of the time, I didn't make the roster. Instead of feeling bad for myself, I would go back and work on my weaknesses. I focused on the things I needed to compete on a national level. The coaches liked me, not just for my skill base, but because I was coachable and a good teammate.

My fitness level was arguably the best of any other player on the Women's National Team. I was always trying to improve. I was always trying to push myself. I was willing to do whatever it took to be the best.

Along the way, I had a ton of injuries. In 2007, I suffered an ACL tear. A lot of people were predicting that my career was over. I had the pressure of other players, more skilled than I, trying to push me out of my starting spot. Despite the setbacks and pressure, I pushed myself to the brink. I overcame my injury. I went from a high probability of not making the team to coming back, starting, and playing absolutely the best soccer of my career.

My last laugh is earning those three Olympic gold medals and a World Cup despite all the obstacles: injuries, weaknesses, and stiff competition.

VISION

It wasn't until I had a conversation about my goals with Mark Krikorian, the coach for the Philadelphia Charge, that the seed was planted for me to be on the Women's National Team. At that point, I set a series of goals.

1. Get an invitation to the Women's' National Team camp.
2. Get invited back a second time.
3. Be a starter.
4. Be a consistent starter.

My goals grew to include winning Olympic gold and then competing for the World Cup. I was able to accomplish everything I set out to accomplish in my soccer career. I have no regrets. Many times, people look back and wish they could've done this or that. Not me. I am very content with everything. I walked away from the sport on my terms.

VALOR

I was injured in 2007 shortly before we were to compete for the World Cup. That was a huge disappointment, but I was determined to get back on the field as soon as possible.

This injury was new territory for me. There were a lot of decisions to be made. I did my homework. I researched my options. I chose a protocol that had risks but also offered a potentially faster recovery. I could not afford any setbacks. I had to listen to my body. I had to really learn. I pushed myself to do whatever it took to get back on the field, and I succeeded.

In 2008, I helped my team win a gold medal. In 2011, I was named to the U.S. roster for the FIFA Women's World Cup Tournament in Germany. I added another gold medal in the 2012 Olympics where I played all ninety minutes of the match against Colombia.

VIGOR

It's a new world. With social media, there is a high potential to read negative stuff about yourself. That negative stuff can do one of two things: it can create self-doubt or it can motivate you. I am the type of person who uses negativity as motivation. That has helped me throughout my career.

My encouragement to others is to use negativity to motivate you. There's this amazing quote, "Tell me I can't and then watch me work twice as hard to prove you wrong." If reading negativity doesn't motivate you, then take my advice: don't read it.

I love accomplishing my goals. I've done it time and time again. When I think back on the negative things that were said about me over the years, it makes me feel even better about my accomplishments.

VITALITY

My mom passed on the value of healthy eating. When I went off to college, I was the person who ate chicken and two vegetables every night. I've always been very mindful of what I put in my body. I knew being healthy and fit gave me the best shot at optimal performance on the field.

Fitness and healthy eating also empowered my pregnancies. After retiring from a seventeen-year professional soccer career, it was only natural for me to stay active throughout my first pregnancy. I was literally working out just two days before giving birth! But once I had my son, I experienced another first: I found it way more challenging than I ever imagined to get back in shape and feel fit.

This was uncharted territory for me, as being extremely fit was my livelihood for my entire adult life. I underestimated how little time and motivation I would have.

I soon became pregnant again and started searching for a great pregnancy workout video to do from the comfort of my home. I wanted an exercise routine that was safe, fun, challenging, and made me feel great about myself and my changing body. I quickly learned there are very few options available for pregnant women. That's why I teamed up with sports physiologist Shannon Grady, who is also a former athlete and mom, and created "Empowered Pregnancy." We want women to feel confident and strong while doing what is best for their baby.

We provide twelve empowering workouts that follow the guidelines of the American Congress of Obstetricians and Gynecologists. We also share health tips and benefits for you and your baby for that extra inspiration.

I'm happy to report my delivery and recovery were much quicker after my second child. I love sharing the concept with new moms and moms like me that want to get and stay fit.

VERACITY

I am honest to a fault. Truth-telling is important. There's not enough of that going on in the world. I speak from my heart. As a coach, I want the best from my players and for my players. Everybody receives criticism differently, so I am sensitive in how I speak the truth. Hopefully, people understand I talk from a place of honesty with the best intentions possible.

VEHEMENCE

I keep my head in the game by setting goals and reviewing them daily. I have ultimate goals which are very lofty and take a lot to get there. I also have attainable goals along the way. I look at it like starting at the bottom and working hard to get to the top. Lofty goals will discourage you if you don't have smaller goals to move you in the right direction.

I'm also motivated by visuals. For example, when I'm on a treadmill, I'm listening to my music and I have a vision in my head. During the time I was trying to make the Women's National Team, I would envision the player who was starting. I would envision what I needed to do to get that position. I would envision how hard my competition was working and how much harder I had to work to earn that position. This helped me press through my tiredness.

I would also watch a highlight reel video before games. Seeing the successful plays and scenes of celebrating after a good game motivated me to do my best.

When I retired, I didn't miss the actual playing as much as is the camaraderie that we enjoyed. Visualizing those moments of success with the celebration that follows really helped me to get out there and do what I needed to do.

VICTORY

I don't celebrate success for long. I celebrate briefly and then it's on to the next goal. That's the life of an athlete. You're never satisfied. I was able to do all the things I wanted to do before I stepped away and started my family. I have accomplished everything I set out to accomplish.

Now that I have my family and my kids? Even though my career was amazing, nothing compares to being a mom. This is the ultimate victory.

Life after sports still has me on the field coaching young athletes and in the office supporting retired athletes and aspiring executives in the pursuit of their goals. I recently founded a company, Ceres Platinum Group, with my friend and co-athlete Angela Hucles. We both played and achieved at the highest levels of our sport. When we decided to leave the playing field, we didn't anticipate some of the new challenges in store for us. As athletes, we are used to having a team to support our efforts. However, off the field, we didn't have the support we needed to manage our lives and set new goals. Ceres Platinum is tailored for female athletes currently playing and retired as well as executives that want a team to assist them in managing their finances and building their careers.

So there are goals to be set and victories to be reached in the days ahead.

Learn more about Heather by visiting her websites, heathermitts.com and ceresplatinumgroup.com; on Twitter at @heathermitts; or on Instagram at @hmitts2 and @empoweredpregnancy.

Ken Mok

"It's far easier to tell the truth than it is to sustain a lie. People who lie have to keep embellishing things and covering their tracks. I don't have to cover my tracks in anything because I'm completely honest and straightforward."

KEN'S VICTORIES

Ken Mok is a television producer and director and the founder and president of 10x10 Entertainment, a production company that produces television, film, and alternative media. Ken's production portfolio is extensive, including hits like *America's Next Top Model*, *The Tiger Woods Story*, and *Stylista*, among other projects. Ken has also directed a number of very successful films, including Vince Papale's life story, *Invincible* (2006), and the Academy Award-nominated film *Joy* (2015).

THE LAST LAUGH

Coach Jim Harbaugh of the Michigan Wolverines said, "You need to set your dreams and goals so high that everybody laughs at them. If nobody is laughing at your dreams and goals, you haven't set them high enough." That's true. If you don't have a dream that people laugh at, that means your dream is not big enough. I think that is the case for anybody who's going to become successful in their field.

The *Invincible* movie, the story of Vince Papale becoming a Philadelphia Eagle against all odds, is transferable to any venture from business to acting. A leader is an outlier by definition. It's the person who doesn't follow the conventional path. It's the person who doesn't follow the crowd. It's someone who thinks differently from the crowd. You will be derided and ridiculed. You will be criticized. People will try to tear you down out of jealousy. Some will deride your idea because they genuinely think you are on the wrong path. "What are you doing? Why are you doing this? You shouldn't be. It's never going to work." The ones who make it are those who don't listen to that.

I've had that throughout my career. When I was growing up, I wanted to be a television producer. I wanted to have my own production company. I didn't know anybody in the entertainment business. Everybody was telling me I was crazy. I was this Asian kid from Larchmont, New York. There were no Asian producers or directors in 1987. In fact, when I became an executive at NBC, I was one of the first Asian guys to have ever held a network executive job. People looked at me like I was an alien. As I was climbing the ladder trying to get where I was going, people left and right were completely dismissive of what I was doing. I had to prove myself. As I shared my ideas and talked creatively, they began to respect me.

When I came up with the idea for *America's Next Top Model*, a rival of mine tried to completely derail the project. That was out of jealousy. He actively tried to sabotage my career. He made calls to agents saying that I was this terrible person. He told them Tyra Banks should not do the show with me.

Fortunately, the people who know me know how I am. They didn't believe the story. They stood up for me and spread the word: "Ken is the most upstanding, straightforward, honest guy that I've ever met. Everything that this other guy is saying is a complete fabrication. Be completely suspicious of the source of these rumors. It doesn't ring true at all." So we moved forward with *America's Next Top Model*, and it totally changed my career. Tyra Banks and I have become close friends. She's the godmother of my children, and I'm the godfather to her son. The guy who tried to undermine me is out of the business now. That's vindication. That's my last laugh.

VISION

I love TV. I love watching movies. When I was a kid, I watched more TV than anyone, to the dismay of my parents. They were freaking out. By the time I was fourteen years old, I knew what I wanted to do in life. I was in my English class and we were watching a foreign film. I don't remember the actual language of the film, but it was expressed visually. I understood that film very clearly in the language of cinema. My teacher gave me positive feedback on the essay I wrote about that film. He told me I had a special talent and saw the film clearly in ways that the other kids didn't. I knew then that's what I wanted to do. I wanted to be a producer with my own production company. I wanted to work in TV. I was very lucky that at that young age I knew what I wanted to do.

That's the key—to discover and follow your passion. Once you have clarity of vision, you must plan out how are you going to get up that mountaintop. It takes many steps to climb a mountain.

I did a lot of research and I worked as much as I could in the industry. I learned that there are certain steps you must take to own your own production company. You have to get your foot in the door. You have to start at the bottom. You have to take that assistant production job on any show you can so that you can learn "the business." Then you have to move up to the next position, whatever that is.

I plotted my path.

My first goal was to get a production assistant job on a TV show in New York so I could survey the landscape. I managed to do that. I got a production assistant job on *The Cosby Show*. This was back in 1989. I had to live at home because I wasn't getting paid a lot of money. It only paid like 300 bucks a week.

My second goal was to get a network job. There, I could oversee TV shows and understand how all that worked. I used my connections at *The Cosby Show* to get into this junior training program at NBC. I became a junior executive.

My third goal was to go from the buying side to the production side. I became a producer. I ended up getting a deal at MTV, becoming a producer and running a production company. After that, I started my own production company, independent of everybody, and created *America's Next Top Model*.

I knew what I wanted to do. I charted out each of the steps I would have to take. I made sure that everything I did in life was to get to that next step. It took me years, but I finally got there. It all worked out.

You must have clarity of vision on what your ultimate goal is. Then you have to figure out the steps to reach your goal. You need to plan your life out accordingly. You need to spend every minute of your day focused on getting to that goal. Put on the blinders. Be like a horse in a horse race.

There is a fascinating documentary on HBO called *The Defiant Ones*. It's the story of Jimmy Iovine and Dr. Dre. These guys kept the blinders on. Iovine started out as a recording engineer, Dre as a DJ. They shed those skins and went on to co-found Interscope Records and Beats by Dre. From there, they shed that skin and went on to co-create Apple Music and they continue to take on new ventures. The principles laid out in the documentary are true. I live by those values. You have to be obsessive about what you are doing in life. Those two men have a clear vision of what they want to accomplish. They use all their resources and all their energy to serve that vision. Everybody who has been a successful leader in whatever industry, whether it be music, acting, or business, has a clarity of vision and are obsessive about it. They don't care what other people think.

VITALITY

I am very ambitious person. Most people at my age are slowing down. I'm speeding up. There are a lot more things I want to do in terms of moviemaking and directing. I want to make this last phase of life the most prolific. And that's what's happening.

I need energy to do it. You have to take care of your body. I work out and watch what I eat. One of the things that helps me keep in shape are my seven-year-old twins. I also have a sixteen-year-old. I had the twins later in life. Most people would be grandparents at this point. They keep my energy going. If you don't have your health, you don't have anything.

VALOR

If I died tomorrow, I would have no regrets. I have helped contribute to the culture. I have helped make the world a better place. Every show that I've done, I have tried to not just make it entertaining. I have chosen projects that have larger-than-life meaning with messages that can inspire people. The movie *Invincible* is prototypical of that. That story inspired people. The message—"If you want it bad enough, you can achieve your dreams"—that's why I did it. It was entertaining, but it was inspirational.

America's Next Top Model is the same thing. I wanted to do a show that was entertaining, but I also wanted to expand the definition of beauty. There are many types of beauty—plus size people, unusual looking people, people who are black, white, Asian, and Latino. I had to fight against the network when the show started. I wanted the cast to be inclusive. At the time, inclusive meant you have one Asian person or one black person in a cast of ten. That was considered diverse. That, to me, is not diverse. Diverse to me is when you have a true mix of people in the cast.

Times have changed. Now diversity in TV is huge. Back then it was not. It was hard to make it happen. I had to put my foot down. I'm really glad I did. If you believe in your principles and you believe in your values, you have to stand up for them. You have to fight for them. Values are not just words. Values are things that you live by. If you live by them, you must have the courage to stand by them.

Living by your values makes you a stronger person. It gives you self-respect. Self-respect gives you the courage to stand up in moments when other people wilt. I've always been a guy who stood by my values in every single project I have done. I have always stood up for what is right and stood against what is wrong. It's made me stronger. I'm not afraid of anything. I'm not afraid of anybody.

VEHEMENCE

I keep my passion stoked by only investing my emotional energy into products I truly believe in. Take the movie *Invincible* for example. When I saw a short video called *Under the Helmet* about Vince's story, I got fired up. When I was pitching *Invincible*, I believed—this story has to be told! This is going to be a hit movie! It's an underdog story. This guy was an amazing guy, a bouncer who went to an open tryout for the Philadelphia Eagles and made the team. He then became special teams captain. I have got to tell this story! That gets other people excited. That's how I got Brad Gann to write the script for free. He saw the story. He talked to Vince and was like, "Oh my god. I'm going to write this script on spec."

Your ability to make things happen as a film producer or a writer is directly related to your passion. All you have in this town are ideas. When you present them to prospective buyers, you better believe in your idea 1,000%, or you will never sell it. I had a meeting last week with a guy who is going to invest in one of the films I'm doing. He saw how excited I was about it. He said, "Your passion translates. I believe in this project because you believe in it so much."

Your job is to convince other people and get them as fired up about your project as you are. I've been able to do that throughout my career. Every project I pick is a labor of love. Every project has been something I've completely gotten behind. When you have that passion within you, when you believe in something so much, it's like you are proselytizing to people. It's like you're the leader of the church and you are getting people to join. That is what has happened with every project I have done. I got people to believe because of my passion.

VIGOR

You have to eliminate the people in your life who are negative. It could be a relative. It could be a friend. If they are draining you and constantly naysaying, you have got to cut them out of your life.

There are lot of frenemies in the world. As I was moving up in the business, I had a friend. He was my best friend. We had been friends since the seventh grade. But he became toxic. He worked in the business but was not achieving the success that I was. As I was moving ahead, he continually tried to undermine me. I realized very clearly what his motivation was. He was jealous. After a while I had to ask myself, "What is this person doing? Why is he doing this? What is his motivation?" Even though this guy had been my friend since I was thirteen years old, I had to cut off the friendship. He was a drain on my energies and my psyche.

Cut out everything that drains your energy. I never read the *Hollywood Reporter* or *Variety*. I don't pay attention to what rival production companies are doing. I don't care. That's energy I can't afford to expend.

VERACITY

If I'm working with you, I'm always going to tell you the truth. It might be good. It might be bad. You might like it. You might not. But I will always be a truth-teller.

I've been in positions where I worked for other people and I didn't know where I stood. I don't know if this guy's blowing smoke up my behind or if I'm doing a good job. I would say to my supervisors, "I just want the truth. Tell me what I'm doing right and what I'm doing wrong. Tell me what I need to work on." Often, I would get the runaround. I decided that once I reach a certain point I will always be straight up and truthful with people. They will know where I stand.

It's easier to live life that way. It's far easier to tell the truth than it is to sustain a lie. People who lie have to keep embellishing things and covering their tracks. I don't have to cover my tracks in anything because I'm completely honest and straightforward. The people who work with me appreciate that.

VICTORY

Amy Chua, author of *Battle Hymn of the Tiger Mom*, has gotten a lot of notoriety because of the way she's raising her kids. Her kids went on to Harvard and Yale and achieved great things. I'm Asian, so I understand what she's doing. Asian families are really focused on education and discipline. Asian parents can be overbearing.

The author says there three things that you need to be really successful.

1. An inferiority complex.
2. A superiority complex.
3. An obsessive work drive.

If you have those three things, you will achieve great things. I have all three of those things. I have an inferiority complex. I worry that I'm not as good as other people. I have a superiority complex. I think that I'm smarter than most. I have this relentless work ethic. Those three things drive me. The inferiority complex pushes me to prove everybody wrong. The superiority complex means believing in what I am doing. I feel smarter than the other people. If other people tell me I am wrong, I know in my mind that I'm right and they're wrong. On top of that, I have this relentless drive. I get up every day and I work my butt off.

I never want to stop achieving. There are a lot of people who have had tremendous success early in their career. They reach a certain point in their life and they stop growing. They're too rich. They've gotten used to this cushy lifestyle. They are resting on their laurels and surrounding themselves with people who are blowing sunshine up their butt. The reason they stop is complacency.

I never want to become complacent. There might be a certain time, like when I'm seventy-five, where I say, "Enough. I want to take a rest." But I'm nowhere close to that. I'm always out there second-guessing myself.

I'm always scraping for the next project. Whenever I achieve success, I set that marker another hundred yards down the field. I go for it again. Once I get close to it, I set the marker further down the field.

I'm always looking for that next thing. I keep an open mind to what's going on in the culture. The worst thing in this business is to not stay connected to the culture. I ask my assistants and other people who are in their 20s, "What games are people playing? Who are the top artists? Help me to become a part of it so I can understand it." I fight every day to stay connected so I can continue to generate ideas and come up with things that are going to make sense as a director, writer, and producer.

I also am always trying new things. I am thinking about learning how to fly. I have a game plan. I'm not going out onto the runway and taking flying lessons. I bought simulator software that teaches me online how to fly a plane. In two years, when I go to my flight instructor to teach me how to fly a plane, I will already know how to fly a plane.

It is never too late to do anything. Whatever you want to do in life, you can do it.

JR Ridinger

"It takes valor to be in the trenches with your people,
but it is where every leader should be."

JR'S VICTORIES

James "JR" Ridinger founded Market America in 1992. He is the architect of the UnFranchise Business Development System, a business model that currently serves around 200,000 hardworking, independent business owners. More than 400 have become millionaires. In a time of economic uncertainty, JR has leveraged Market America and Shop.com into a recession-proof business offering in-demand, market-driven products and services. It's called the UnFranchise and is a hybrid of online retailing and direct sales.

THE LAST LAUGH

I was a marine biologist. The government sent me to find plagues in fishing banks. I would spend days at high sea studying diseases on fish. I thought I was going to be like a Jacques Cousteau, until one day we went from New Jersey to the Bahamas with some friends. I noticed the beautiful houses and yachts. I asked who they belonged to. "They belong to entrepreneurs," they told me. I had never heard the word before, but I thought, "I want to be an entrepreneur." Around that time, while doing research, I had a near-death experience. I almost got washed overboard. That experience changed the direction of my life. I decided that being a marine biologist was not for me.

Call it luck or divine providence, but coming off that experience, I was introduced to the network marketing industry. The industry was based on the idea of building a team of people who market products through relationships, bypassing the middleman and earning a percentage of the sales generated by the team. In theory, it made so much sense. I took to the idea of being in control of my financial future.

I pursued a career in network marketing and was very successful. Sadly, I was one of only a few who did succeed. It became clear to me that the system was flawed. It wasn't realistic for the average person to succeed no matter how hard they tried. This high failure rate was leaving a trail of destruction.

I walked away from the business and was hired as a consultant to the direct selling industry. I shared with my wife, Loren, my disillusionment with the system. I knew there was a better way. She persuaded me to take a leap of faith and start a company that would fix those flaws I saw.

Transforming my vision and philosophy into math and logic using computerization was going to be a big job.

These were the essentials:

- A compensation system that offered people—regardless of background, bank account, color, or gender—the opportunity to become financially fit by working part-time for 2–3 years.

- A business based on the strengths of franchising—a duplicable system that provides training, tools, and branding while eliminating stiff start-up costs and ongoing royalties.

- Marketplace agility so we could quickly adjust our product and service offerings as the demand shifted. We would call it "The Mall Without Walls."

- The ability for independent contractors (referred to as UnFranchise owners) to customize a business based on their specific interests and goals by offering businesses within the business. We provide the products, services, technology, and training. They find the customers.

- Access to state-of-the-art technology, offering the ability to manage and scale each distributor's business.

It was no easy task to nail down the specifics. Together, with the help of friends who had actuarial and programming skills, we transformed the vision and philosophy into a new math and logic-based model. The Market America UnFranchise was born. It was a hybrid that included all the essentials.

Everybody would see it and rejoice, right? Wrong.

The Direct Selling Association hated me. "How dare you try to change an industry that has been around for fifty years."

People thought I was crazy. Maybe we were crazy. We had very little start-up capital. Our office was on our kitchen table. My employees were my wife and my brother-in-law. They had to work for free. We had one product, a crappy piece of jewelry, to sell. As far as technology, the internet was in its infancy and computers were not a household essential yet.

But there was no scarcity of belief. Beyond belief, I had a "knowing." I knew this would work. It was an idea whose time had come.

There were two things in our favor.

- People, regardless of demographic, will always shop. We were going to provide the things they wanted to buy.

- People are always looking for a way to improve their financial position. We were going to provide them with a mathematically-sound, duplicable system for matching people to products and products to people and the ability to earn a good living doing so.

We were resisted every step of the way, but we did not turn back.

Now, twenty-five years later, we are enjoying the last laugh. We have nearly 200,000 UnFranchise owners in ten countries and over 400 millionaires. We offer more than one thousand exclusively-branded products drawn from fourteen major industries and fifty million affiliate products through a shopping portal that tracks purchases and flawlessly tabulates and credits commissions and retail profit to the independent UnFranchise owner. We offer businesses within the business for weight loss coaches, makeup artists, musicians, website and financial consultants, non-profit fundraisers, health professionals, and more. We have retail sales exceeding 8 billion dollars with more than half of that paid out to our UnFranchise owners in retail profits and commissions. We have an A plus rating with the Better Business Bureau. We earned the BBB coveted Torch Award for Marketplace Excellence. We were ranked in the top 100 internet retailers worldwide.

I set out to correct the flaws of an old industry. Along the way, I created a new industry. My only regret is I did not patent our system. Dozens of companies have tried to reverse-engineer us, and some of them have created messes along the way.

The success of Market America, despite the naysayers, is a last laugh, but I am in the middle of creating another. There's a power that is greater than politics, greater than philosophies, and greater than the atom bomb. It's people power. I plan on re-creating an economy that is based on people power—*people working together collectively to get something done.*

I refuse to participate in the current economy that is based on archaic and inequitable means of wealth distribution. Together with other UnFranchise owners, we are in the process of maturing a concept called the Shopping Annuity where people can get paid on everything they purchase.

It's in its beginning stages. In 2011, we purchased Shop.com, a shopping site developed by some of the most brilliant minds in Silicon Valley. We are improving the technology to make it very easy for consumers to shop, and we are developing financial incentives to do so.

People will be hearing soon about the Shop.com Shopping Annuity. By participating in this collective economy, our UnFranchise owners will be able to withstand the turbulence of the nation's economy. Yes, people will laugh and resist, but I not only believe we will revolutionize the way people can create income by converting their spending into earning, I know this is an idea whose time is come. Nothing's going to stop it.

VISION

Think big, as you will never be bigger than your thoughts. The greatest realization in life for me was that we literally become what we think about. We can manifest our dreams through the law of creation.

To those dreams, we have to add two things: emotion (passion and desire) and logic (math and science). If you don't have logic, the subconscious mind will argue with the conscious mind that you can't do that. Your conscious mind needs to be able to explain to the subconscious mind why it can be done. The logic will help to support the emotions you have attached to your dream. This is especially important when everybody around you is beating you up, telling you it can't be done. You will fold if you don't have a foundation of logic.

As you break down your dream into daily, weekly, and monthly actions, it's amazing. You will begin to attract the answers and circumstances for it to be manifested into reality. I am so attuned to this that it just happens. It's amazing. I have to be very careful what I think about because I'll attract it.

VITALITY

The more successful you become, there is a great temptation to not do what you need to do to stay healthy. That is a big mistake. You must never stop paying attention to your physical health. If you don't feel good, you have an excuse for not doing anything.

I run twice a week. I also do something physical—swim, cycle 10–15 miles, or ski—but my religion is yoga. I do extreme yoga. I do drawbacks, handstands, and all types of very difficult stuff. I put yoga before everything else. When I schedule yoga, everybody knows to get out of the way. I will not let anything interfere with that time. The biggest reason I am committed to yoga is not so much the body but the mind. Yoga centers me.

Physical activity clears my mind and reduces stress and anxiety. It also treats my mental constipation. I receive the greatest ideas and solutions when I am working out or doing yoga. The answers just come to me. That's a good reason to do it.

VALOR

You cannot lead where you will not go and you cannot teach what you do not know. Those executives who sit in their ivory tower really don't know what's happening on the front line. In my business, I set it up so the corporate team are also UnFranchise owners. I was advised that this could create a conflict of interest. I considered it a conflict of interest if they aren't in the trenches with a vested interest in the outcome.

We are currently expanding internationally. I have an organization in the United Kingdom. I went there personally to help build it. I did six meetings a day for weeks. I want to face the same problems my team faces. I want to know the issues so we can help solve them.

It takes valor to be in the trenches with your people, but it is where every leader should be. I also believe in the warning, "Don't forget where you came from." In the trenches, I am continually reminded of where I came from when I spend time with people who are just getting started. I never want to lose touch with that.

It takes valor to make the right decisions. In our corporate board meetings, when presented with an opportunity, we ask first, "Is this good for the UnFranchise owner?" Even if the corporation could benefit, if it would hurt our field, we will walk away from that opportunity.

VEHEMENCE

Problems will come and go, but you need the vehemence and passion to stay the course.

What keeps me vehement? I know I can change the world by helping to change people's economic future. That's what keeps me focused. I'm driven to identify what will help people secure the financial foundation they need to live the life they want to live. No amount of naysaying can tear me down. That's my Why.

If you want people to follow you, first tell them your Why. Help them find their Why for following. I don't like to give orders. I don't like to tell people what to do. I don't want to be their boss. I want to be their leader. I want them to find their Why. If they find their Why, then the How is easy. Everything will fall into place. Circumstances will begin to present themselves to help you get where you want to go.

VIGOR

Too many people sit around and watch dumb reality shows on TV or fall into Twitter wars. All that crap is going to get you nowhere. Dreams are hungry. They need to be fed. If you don't feed them, they lose their vigor. They die.

One way I feed my dreams is by listening to audios and reading books. I have fed my mind with audios and/or books every day for the last thirty-five years. Though I don't have time to read much these days—at 6 a.m. every morning, I am met with a stack of about five inches of paper— I listen to my books on audio. As I listen, I get some great ideas. I begin to put my own twist on these ideas. The material I consume also gives me some interesting things to share with others. If you have something great to say, people will listen to you.

As you pursue your vision, people are not always going to be supportive. Often, your closest friends and family will discourage you.

Why? Because if you actually succeed, you expose their mediocrity and their failure. It is easier to discourage you than to deal with their failure and mediocrity. It's easier to beat you down so you don't do it. That is going to happen to every single person who tries to excel.

Audios and books program the mind and encourage mental toughness. They also provide a mental vacation from negative people. It will help you stay the course to success. The greatest last laugh is your success.

VERACITY

You will know the truth, and the truth shall set you free. Being straight up and honest is not always easy, but there is no shortcut. If you walk in truth, there is nothing to argue or hide. Facts are facts. It is what it is.

Don't lie to someone to get their business. If what you have to offer is not for them, that's okay.

Be who you are. Hypocrisy (a.k.a. play-acting) is a poison that will bring you down. It's a cancer. If it starts to spread, you are in big trouble. It will consume you.

Stay humble. Don't become high and mighty. When you become successful, don't forget where you came from, or you might not be able to find your way back home. When you do something wrong, don't get defensive. Admit it.

Stay relevant. Change and adapt with the time. You might be totally right, but no matter your high and mighty pontificating, if you are not relevant, you're going to disintegrate.

Be sincere. Address issues with people head-on. Do not allow problems to percolate. Sincerity is the great equalizer. People will receive what you have to say if you are sincere.

VICTORY

This is victory for me. I look at so many people and I realize it's very unlikely they would to be able to make it on their own. A vehicle is not going to drop out of the sky for them to improve their financial future. Life's going to pass them by. When someone wakes up and sees what I see and joins me in the journey, that's a win. That's victory.

People ask me, did you ever expect to be where you are, CEO of a highly successful company that has helped so many others realize their dreams? The answer is yes! That is what gave me the stamina to keep going. Admittedly, I thought I was climbing a hill, and it turns out I was l climbing Mount Everest, the tallest mountain in the world, but by the time I realized it, I was halfway there. I had to keep going. Inch by inch, blood, sweat, and tears the whole way. I am so grateful and thankful when I achieve a victory.

But there's always another mountain. Call me crazy if you want, but I believe that we can change the world through entrepreneurialism. The internet and digital world change everything, and the economy is no longer controlled strictly by supply and demand.

We can create our own economic ecosystem and sub-economies by working together and growing through cooperation rather than competition. Government, politics, or ideologies cannot solve the world's problems. The only solution is through economic opportunity—making money with each other. No one is going to shoot his or her pay check!

I teach my team that if you want to be successful, identify a trend or paradigm shift that will change the future. Position yourself to lead the parade rather than getting in at the tail end. Creating an entrepreneurial opportunity based on something everyone does (shop) can change the economic future.

So I am still climbing and encouraging others to do the same.

Every salutation on every email and letter is "keep growing." If you are not growing, it's over. Through success and every failure, keep climbing. If you have a strong Why supported by logic and passion, it is just a matter of time.

To learn more about JR, Market America, and the UnFranchise, visit beingjrridinger.com.

Brian Rutenberg

*"People ask me what happens when I feel uninspired.
The answer is nothing. Inspiration is unreliable. The
only thing I can rely on is a work schedule. When I feel
blocked, I keep painting because that's my job."*

BRIAN'S VICTORIES

Widely considered to be one of the finest American painters of his generation, Brian Rutenberg has spent forty years honing a distinctive method of compressing the rich color and form of his native coastal South Carolina into complex landscape paintings that imbue material reality with a deep sense of place.

He is a Fulbright Scholar, a New York Foundation for the Arts Fellow, a Basil Alkazzi USA Award recipient, an Irish Museum of Modern Art visiting artist program participant, and has had over two hundred exhibitions throughout North America.

Rutenberg's paintings are included in such museum collections as Yale University Art Gallery, The Butler Institute of American Art, Bronx Museum of Art, Peabody Essex Museum of Art, Greenville County Museum of Art, Provincetown Art Association and Museum, South Carolina State Museum, and many others. His popular YouTube videos, called "Brian Rutenberg Studio Visits," are viewed daily by people all over the world.

Radius Books published a full color monograph of his work in 2008. Brian's new book, *Clear Seeing Place*, is an Amazon #1 bestseller.

Brian lives and works in New York City with his wife Kathryn and their two children.

THE LAST LAUGH

I live in NYC. I have been here thirty years. In the 90s, I was living on peanut butter Cap'n Crunch and sweet iced tea. I would send my slides to galleries almost every day—hundreds of slides—and almost all of them were returned to me.

One day, I had a message on my answering machine from a prominent New York dealer. He wanted me to come to his gallery in person. Could this be my big break? I got a haircut, showered, and put on my most luxurious black turtleneck. I took the R train to Prince Street in SoHo. I bounded into the gallery and introduced myself to the receptionist, a dour little man wearing an even more luxurious black turtle neck. Without making eye contact, he held out my slides with a post-it note signed by the gallery owner that read, "Don't let this guy come near me." I was humiliated.

Pain is a great teacher. One of my favorite quotes is by Mike Tyson: "Everyone has a plan until they get punched in the mouth."

Ten years later, that same dealer expressed an interest in my work. Yes, I did what any self-respecting artist would do: I wrote "Go F*** yourself" on a Post-it and sent it back to him.

That was indeed one of those last laugh moments, but the ultimate last laughs are the lessons I have learned along the way. I had a wonderful mentor to teach me those lessons. He was the British painter Michael Tyzack, my professor at the College of Charleston. Michael had a generosity of spirit. He was my "other father" who exposed me to experiences where I learned what a true professional looked like.

During my senior year at the College of Charleston, world-renowned environmental artists Christo and Jeanne-Claude flew down from New York City for a lecture and exhibition. Michael asked me to drive him to the airport to meet them. I chauffeured Michael and the artists downtown for a Lowcountry lunch of barbecue, chicken bog, buttery, buttery biscuits, and sweet tea.

Christo and Jeanne-Claude were so kind. I was a tall, goofy, nineteen-year-old nobody sitting face-to-face with two international art stars, yet they spoke to me with respect. They made eye contact, asked questions about my work, and listened to my responses. They even gave me their private number to call when in New York. They inspired me. After lunch, I ran to my studio and painted for twenty-four hours straight. I couldn't wait to meet more visiting artists.

Later that year, another well-known painter, who had appeared in a recent Whitney Biennial exhibition of contemporary American art, flew from New York for another lecture and exhibition. Once again, Michael chose me to drive him to the airport to pick her up. He introduced me as his finest student. The artist responded by shoving her luggage in my face. She did not make eye contact and spoke to me like I was a small animal.

I was dejected. I remember going to Michael's office that night. I actually cried. Unlike Jeanne-Claude and Christo, she made me feel like a phony. Michael winked and said he was teaching me a valuable lesson that I'd have to figure out on my own.

Flash forward twenty years. I shared a tearful goodbye with Michael as he lay dying of cancer. His wife, Ann, held the phone to his ear. He was too weak to talk. I told him, "I realize what you had to teach me years ago." Michael didn't bring me along to the airport those many years ago to have me help with the luggage. He brought me along to show me how a professional artist treats a nobody. Christo and Jean-Claude had nothing to gain by showing me kindness and respect. They did it because that's what pros do. When confronted by arrogance, Michael taught me to stand ten feet tall and be bulletproof.

Working in the arts in New York City for thirty years has enabled me to meet a lot of famous, successful people, and they have one thing in common: good manners. They are consummate professionals with nothing to prove outside of their craft because everything goes into it. Nothing is left over. The dicks are the ones who have something to prove outside of their work, and I've met plenty. To them, I say, "Thank you for showing me how not to behave. "

To this day, I answer every email. I make time to speak to artists who approach me. I see their shows when I can and I treat every single one with dignity. I try to instill that generosity of spirit in my children. I learned that from Michael. Maybe I am his last laugh.

If you ever visit the College of Charleston campus, you will see three paintings prominently hung in the entrance to the School of the Arts: William Halsey on the left, Michael Tyzack on the right, and me in between.

VISION

Every creative person should define their job description. A label is our best friend. The narrower your footprint, the broader the umbrella over you. I always ask art students, "What is your job, exactly?" The word "artist" doesn't mean anything. Every pinhead who bakes gourmet cookies is an artist. I am not an artist, not a painter, not even a landscape painter, but a Southern landscape painter who lives and works in New York City. That's my superpower under the sun. Art students are frightened into thinking that they must be original right out of the gate or risk mediocrity. They are pressured into growing and evolving. Those are art school bullshit words. There is great breadth and poetry in repetition, in doing the same thing for a long time. That's how you get really good at stuff. No one talks about that.

Duke Ellington said, "The wise musicians are those who play what they can master."

VITALITY

I suffer from obstructive apnea, a sleep disorder in which the soft tissue in the back of my throat collapses during sleep, forcing my brain to produce a shock of adrenaline to wake me up to breathe. Over decades, a lack of REM sleep puts a dangerous strain on the heart, not to mention other lovely side effects like depression, high blood pressure, and memory loss. For the rest of my life, I have to wear a continuous positive airway pressure mask while I sleep. A CPAP is basically a fat person breathing machine that keeps my airway open, allowing me to get the deep, restorative sleep I need to function and paint.

I find great comfort in rituals, so my daily schedule is ironclad. I wake up at 7 a.m. and make school lunch for my kids. Then, four days a week, I hit the gym for about thirty minutes of cardio on the treadmill and light lifting. Next is coffee and oatmeal with three buddies at the local diner. We laugh, make fun of each other, talk about our kids, and drink gallons of black coffee. Having breakfast with guy friends consistently is necessary to my sanity. I get to my studio at 10 a.m. and spend the first hour on paperwork and correspondence, after which I stand up and perform a series of stretches developed during my years as a drummer.

Here is my routine: remove socks and shoes, sit down in a hard chair, and cross one leg over the other to form a T. Lean forward slowly to stretch the thighs. Repeat with the other leg. Stand and bow forward, trying not to bend the legs. Slip hands under feet, if possible. Come back to standing and reach towards the ceiling, keeping the shoulders down, and wiggle fingers vigorously. Do ten slow windmills with each arm. Sit and slap the bottoms of the feet. Start painting.

VALOR

Shortly after moving to New York City, I was in a downtown studio with the art historian/critic Clement Greenberg and a few friends. Mr. Greenberg gathered us in a circle and asked, "Who here is a painter?" My hand shot up instinctively. He peered over his bifocals and said, "OK, you can leave." The room fell silent as I awkwardly made my way to the staircase with a lump in my throat. My brain didn't know whether to make anger or tears. At the bottom stair, I realized something that changed my life; as if I'd turned on windshield wipers in a storm, suddenly everything appeared clear and close. Don't be the first to raise your hand. Don't be so sure. There will always be someone better than you, but there can never be anyone like you. At the bottom of a staircase in a downtown loft in 1988, I gave myself permission to stop trying so hard and just be with paint. When I learned to expect nothing, I got everything.

VEHEMENCE

When my daughter asked if I was the tooth fairy, I said, "Yes, honey, I am the fairy."

She thought for a moment. "You fly all over the world and collect the children's teeth?"

My heart filled with joy because we saw the same thing from two different vantage points. To an adult, a child's toy is trivial. However, the world that child creates around it is rich and spacious. I don't know about you, but my childhood was spent in blissful boredom, fishing in lakes and wandering along creek beds with nothing to do; a single day seemed to last forever. There were no plans, only happenings. Ask any kid to describe their day, and they'll say, "This happened. Then this happened. Then that happened." Painting restores the spaciousness of childhood and reminds us of things we knew but forgot, because art is carefully orchestrated wandering. If you're in a hurry, you'll miss everything. To be a painter, you must have more patience than anyone else in the room and know how to disappear in plain view. Becoming a father taught me both. Plus, how seriously can you take yourself while wiping someone's boogers on a tree?

I'm paraphrasing Johnny Carson, who said, "If you're on television long enough, you'll end up doing everything you've ever done." Every painting I make taps into everything I've ever done, every place I've been, and everyone I've met along the way. The longer I live, the richer the soil.

VIGOR

If you want a long career in the arts, then become your own best friend—period. Keep your expenses modest and expectations low. If your studio isn't big, make small work. If your day job doesn't allow enough time to paint, then wake up earlier. Seek out experiences. If someone offers you tickets to the opera, take them. If they ask you to help their dirtball friend move boxes in a garage, do it. If there is a lecture on beavers at the museum, go there. See what life looks like. It takes effort to become expansive.

People ask me what happens when I feel uninspired. The answer is nothing. Inspiration is unreliable. The only thing I can rely on is a work schedule. When I feel blocked, I keep painting because that's my job. Day after day, I hack away at the gigantic, slow-moving iceberg in my studio. When a piece breaks off, I get a painting. That isn't luck, but stubborn persistence. The secret is to show up, no matter how dreadful the results. Comedian Steve Martin said, "It's easy to be great, it's hard to be good." The key is consistency.

VERACITY

Freedom has a taste; it's wild and untamed. The trick is to be able to walk around all day and roll that taste around in your mouth. When you speak, some of the wild may come dribbling out, but it's okay, you'll make more. At night, when you lay your head down on your pillow, you can feel the wild sloshing around in your brain and pooling up behind your eyelids like an incoming moon tide, so that, when you open your eyes, the wild gushes out into the world. Artists are damaged people. We make stuff and ask, "Do you like it?" However, our paycheck is the wild. You know the taste. Collectors don't pay good money for my paintings to see me make measured and responsible decisions. They pay to see me waste my time in wild and delicious ways. Artists live so that others may feel alive.

VICTORY

Every painting fails before it succeeds. Learning to embrace and even orchestrate failure instead of fear it will make you ten feet tall and bulletproof. I still keep a pillowcase full of rejection letters in my studio as a reminder of the role that failure played in galvanizing me. There are many things to fear in life—plane crashes, viruses, bagel pizza— but there is no upside to a fear of failure. It's ok to screw up, just do it gloriously.

John Lennon said, "No one can harm you, feel your own pain." Without negativity, you can't be delusional, and self-delusion is what makes art possible, for every creative endeavor begins in a flash of googly-eyed crazy. How could human beings perform delicate brain surgery or write string quartets without first believing that they mattered and are going to live forever? My early paintings were awful. I never wanted to be great, just less awful. Success is too often confused with popularity; it's gross that a film has to make $100 million to be successful. Art doesn't work that way. True success is curiosity and effort. Popularity is given and taken away by others, but curiosity and effort are yours alone.

To learn more about Brian Rutenberg and his work, upcoming projects, and ideas, visit brianrutenbergart.com.

Coach Dick Vermeil

"I think I have an ability to see in people sometimes what they don't see in themselves. And I've been able to convince them that they have this within them."

COACH VERMEIL'S VICTORIES

Dick Vermeil has had one of the most distinguished coaching careers in the history of the NFL. Vermeil spent fifteen seasons as an NFL head coach, most notably as the head coach of the Philadelphia Eagles, St. Louis Rams (with whom he won Super Bowl XXXIV), and the Kansas City Chiefs, and he was a member of the league's coaching fraternity for nineteen seasons. He brought two teams to the Super Bowl and has also enjoyed a prestigious career as a football broadcaster, analyzing both NFL and college games.

THE LAST LAUGH

I grew up in an agricultural community in Calistoga, California. I was not raised in a sophisticated family. Neither of my parents graduated from high school. My father made a living working very hard and it wasn't a forty-hour week. He worked seven days a week at the old garage right behind the house. We grew up understanding what hard work was. He used to say, "Hard work is not a form of punishment."

My dad was tough and ornery. My mother was the compassionate and empathetic one. I can't tell you how many times my dad would be working on a car into the evening for some guy who lived two hours away. My mom would invite the stranger to dinner. They would be served this great home-cooked meal and some good red wine made by my grandfather Vermeil.

The value of hospitality followed me into my coaching career. At nineteen years old, I married Carol. People thought we were too young at the time, but we have now been married sixty-one years. That is kind of a last laugh, too.

Just like my mom, Carol has fed almost every college and NFL football player I have ever coached. It's amazing how much you can learn about the people you're going to work with when you sit around the dinner table. We shared a glass of wine together and talked about their families and how they were raised. We talked about what they wanted to do with their lives and the setbacks they've had to overcome.

People ask me why I coached the way I coached. It's because of the way I was raised. I was raised to work hard and extend hospitality. It's just me.

Over the years, you experience a lot of last laughs. You know the Vince Papale story. That was a last laugh, but another stand-out is the Kurt Warner story.

I had the opportunity to give Kurt Warner the chance he deserved to play for the Rams. Kurt Warner had been cut from the Green Bay Packers, where he had been a fourth string quarterback. To earn a living, he stocked shelves at a grocery store in Iowa. He moved on to play in the Arena Football League. He matured as a player and then moved on to compete for a spot with NFL Europe. A lot of people were overlooking him, but I saw something in him that was special.

In 1998, the night before final cuts, the biggest question was, "Who would be the Rams' third-string quarterback?" I polled my staff and the votes were split down the middle. The final decision was mine, and I chose Kurt Warner. After I informed him he made the team, I said, "I feel there is something special about you. Something different. And I can't wait to find out what it is."

It was during an exhibition game against San Diego that Trent Green, our starting quarterback, was taken out due to a knee injury. We put Warner in to replace him. I told the team, "Losing Trent is not an excuse for playing poorly. We are going to be a good football team. Warner is going to be our guy." That was the start of Kurt's emergence as a quarterback. I was confident that Warner was a quarterback we could win with. I did not realize he would become a quarterback that we would win because of. Kurt proceeded to play sixteen games into the playoffs and take us to the Super Bowl. He performed well beyond our expectations. From there, he quarterbacked himself right on into the NFL Hall of Fame.

Kurt said something during his induction speech that sums up the last laugh: "Coach, you know I love you. And I'm indebted to you for giving me that chance. I spent my entire career trying to prove you right. In a business run by head decisions, thanks for following your heart." That was one of my last laughs. I followed my heart.

VISION

I think I have an ability to see in people sometimes what they don't see in themselves. And I've been able to convince them that they have this within them. It's intuition based on experience.

For example, people ask me, "How do you know what makes a good quarterback?" I know what one looks like. I had all-conference quarterbacks in high school. I had a junior college all-conference quarterback. I had college and All-American quarterbacks. I had an All-Pro quarterback in Ron Jaworski. I had Kurt Warner, a Hall of Famer from the Rams. I know what a good quarterback looks like. I go by what I see, not what I hear and read. Not what those computerized numbers say. I go by what I have seen on a daily basis. Sooner or later, you've got to go by what you see.

Once I have a vision for a player, I focus on what they can do, not on what they can't do. I work out the way to get the best out of them. I have led a team to a world championship with a number of kids who were college free agents. They weren't drafted players. If all I did was tell them, "God, I can't wait till we draft a player to take your place," they would probably fulfill my negative comments and not fulfill their talents. People have a high tolerance for genuine praise. Not wholesale praise, but praise that is deserved. It is impossible to add value to a person you continually devalue. People will return to you the feelings that you create in them.

Yes, I drove my guys. I worked their asses off. I drove them harder than any other NFL coach at that time. Everyone understood the reason I was doing it. It was because I cared. As Eleanor Roosevelt said, and I often repeat, "People don't care how much you know til they know how much you care." I wanted to help my team be the best that they could be. I cared about my guys. Very few people can give their best on a consistent basis to somebody they don't feel cares about them.

To succeed at anything, you have to define your vision, your value system, and your process. You've got to draw a map for yourself. This map will take you where you want to go. Now, the road might be a little tough from time to time. The road to the Super Bowl is always under construction—it's the same thing in your life.

You have to go to work. You have to work hard. Hard work is a solution. Hard work is a problem solver. There's a close correlation between a superior work ethic and success in life.

VITALITY

I am continually stopped and asked, "Coach, how do you stay looking so good at age eighty?" I tease everybody and tell them the secret is my Napa Valley red wine.

The truth is, I remain in good shape because I make an investment in my health on a continual basis. Nobody's going to do that for you. No coach. No trainer. You've got to take responsibility for that yourself. I see so many people more worried about making a contribution to an investment fund than to their own personal health. Hell, you can't spend it even if you make it if you're not in good health.

I'm lifting the same weights in my fitness routine today that I lifted fifteen years ago. I do circuit weight training on a stationary machine. That routine includes pre-stretching and abdominal exercises three times a week. My entire program takes about forty-five minutes. I alternate between lower and upper body. This forces my heart to pump blood to different areas of my body during the workout, so I'm getting a pretty good cardio workout too. I have not lost any strength. I have not changed my regimen as the years have passed by. When I miss my routine, I feel guilty.

I was raised around the dinner table. I love good food, so I have to control my desire to eat too much. I eat a light breakfast: for example, a protein shake with a multigrain piece of toast. I would rather eat hot cakes and waffles or bacon, eggs, and hash browns every morning. I also eat a light lunch, rather than a large sandwich with potato salad. I'm not active enough anymore to burn those kinds of calories.

To stay in shape physically, you have to be mentally focused first. You have to go through an evaluation process to determine what is important to you and your family. Keeping myself healthy allows me the opportunity to pass on what I have learned. I do not want to become a diminishing value as I get older. Last week, I was in Nebraska speaking to the state coach's convention. Did I go there because of money? No, not at all. I went because I want to remain active. It provides an opportunity for me to feel that I still have some value to share with others.

VALOR

I have been asked many times what the toughest decision I ever had to make in my career was. The first was to step down from the head coach position with the Eagles in 1982. The second was to go back into coaching in 1997 with the St. Louis Rams. Those were two tough decisions. I had left the Eagles because I was emotionally burned out. I had spent seven years working 18–20 hour days. I often slept on a cot in my office. I was my own worst enemy. I burned out.

During those "retirement" years, I worked for CBS and ABC sports in football broadcasting. While I was in broadcasting, my mother would tell me, "Dick, you are going to go back into coaching."

I said, "Mom, why do you say that?"

She said, "You didn't get done what you wanted to get done. You wanted to win the Super Bowl. I think you're going to go back and I think you're going to win one someday."

Well, she ended up being right. I signed a contract with the St. Louis Rams in 1997. In 1999, we won the Super Bowl. That was the same year I was named NFL Coach of the Year for the second time. The first time I had earned the Coach of the Year award was nineteen years earlier, during my time with the Eagles.

Now, I regret that I left the Rams after winning it all. I should've stayed. Do I dwell on it? No. I went on to accept the opportunity to coach the Kansas City Chiefs. I retired five years later. I recognized that when I was tired, my mind didn't work as well as it used to. When you are coaching in the NFL, you are always tired.

I've never taken over a winning football team—two of the three teams I took over were not only losing games, but they had created a losing culture. My job was to change that culture. I think I could go back today, even at my age, and do a better job as a head coach. I know myself better. I understand the process better. I have studied what other great leaders who have led in intense environments have done. I have learned a lot about where I made mistakes and how to correct them. Being better as a coach just means being better as a true leader. I think I would be a better leader now.

VEHEMENCE

My greatest motivators were the kids I coached and would be again today if I was still coaching. Personally, I always felt it was my job to help them be the best they could be. My wife looks at me and laughs. She says, "Nothing fires you up more than being around your former players." That's true. I can't help myself. That's just the way it is. I'm not embarrassed about it. There have been times when I teared up around those guys. They know I care about them and I know they care about me. We share a great experience. We share a great philosophy. And we share a vision of what's important in life.

VIGOR

Read good books. I have read more books since I retired then I have read in my entire life. Good books provide you with an opportunity to reinforce your positive beliefs and correct the things you are doing wrong. I love having my philosophy reinforced by somebody who's done great things with his life. The more people who validate what you believe, the more strongly you believe.

I'm now reading a book called *The Way of the SEAL* by Mark Divine. I thought it was so good that I sent copies to fellow coaches in the NFL. It's a great read for anybody, not just a coach. There is a learning experience on every page. The book shares the tactics and successful secrets of America's elite force.

I learned the Navy SEALs are told not to listen to the news more than twenty minutes a day. Why? Negativity will influence their performance. If you want to know what's going badly in the world, just turn on CNN. That's why ESPN has been so successful. Unlike so many news outlets that love to get the latest scandal or scoop, ESPN offers stories about people who are excelling.

Don't just avoid negative news. Stay away from negative people. I don't care how much money a guy makes. If they are a pain, I don't want to be around them. Negativity will ruin your day.

VERACITY

To succeed in life, you need to be sincere and truthful. You need to treat people like you want to be treated.

There's an old expression that is really true—if you have integrity, nothing else matters. If you don't have integrity, nothing else matters. If you have integrity, even if people don't agree with you, they know what you are saying is true. People who lack integrity will go from one big mistake to another. I've seen this over and over again. If you don't have integrity, you don't have anything, more so today than ever because there are no secrets.

You cannot establish credibility without being evaluated as honest. If you have credibility in your organization, if your people have learned to trust you, they will cover for you even when you make mistakes. They will make you look smarter than you are. It's happened to me many times.

Make sure you are a good example to others. The better example you are as a person, the more good examples you're going to find around you. I prided myself in having had a locker room full of men who were good examples to each other.

VICTORY

A Super Bowl ring is more than just a piece of jewelry. It is a symbol of what people are capable of doing when they work together. I am proud of that ring, but there are symbols that are far more meaningful. I was at a Washington, D.C. event, wearing my world championship Super Bowl ring, and I was sitting next to a man wearing a Medal of Honor—the highest military award in America. My Super Bowl ring had diamonds all over it. There were no diamonds on that Medal of Honor. Yet I realized that Medal of Honor, even without diamonds, had far more real meaning and value than my Super Bowl ring.

One of the most powerful characteristics of a fine leader is humility. An example would be Kurt Warner's induction into the Pro Football Hall of Fame when he acknowledged Trent Green, the injured quarterback he had replaced. This is what he said about Trent:

Our paths crossed in the most incredible of ways, and I acknowledge you could easily be the one standing up here tonight. But the class that you showed while dealing with the toughest of situations is etched in my mind. Your willingness to share your football secrets so I could succeed was incredibly valuable. But the character you displayed, and the way you modeled the definition of teammate, was priceless. Those lessons followed me the rest of my career. Thanks for sharpening my character with yours.

Now that's humility.

For those of you who would like to experience some wonderful Napa Valley wine, visit Vermeil Wines at www.vermeilwines.com.

CLOSING THOUGHTS

We aren't anything special: two average guys with above-average drive. We were born to ordinary families. They had no silver spoons to offer us, but they gave us strong values, discipline, and a solid work ethic.

Over the past forty years, these two average guys, equipped with what we were given, managed to rise from bouncers to pro football players to millionaire success stories. Some consider us lucky. We consider our luck to be preparation colliding with opportunity.

Pay attention to how the code impacted our experiences and the experiences of the elite performers featured in our Hall of Fame. Those seven words—Vision, Valor, Vehemence, Veracity, Vitality, Vigor, and Victory—when understood, can change the course of your life.

Far too many people fall short of their vision, not due to lack of talent or effort, but because they do not have a code to guide their journey. As a result, they waste their energy working the wrong plan, hanging out with the wrong people, and doing the wrong things.

Our hope is that the Victor's Code will help you get clear on your vision. We hope it will guide your efforts in achieving that vision. We hope it will fortify the character and attitude you need to reach your goals. We hope it will keep you powerfully focused, yet light on your feet so you are able to embrace unexpected opportunities presented along the way.

Our ultimate last laugh is helping you defy the odds, silence the naysayers, overcome the obstacles in your head and in your life, and enjoy your last laugh.

RECOMMENDED RESOURCES

For more information on Vince and Dennis, visit lastlaughplaybook.com, where you'll find our calendar, press kits, and booking information. Loved the book? We want to hear from you. Send us a note at info@lastlaughplaybook.com.

LEARN MORE ABOUT THE PEOPLE WHO MADE THIS BOOK POSSIBLE:

Dennis Franks—dennisfranks.com

Vince Papale—vincepapale.com

Bonnie Church—bonniechurch.com

Pat Croce—patcroceandcompany.com

Bo Eason—boeason.com

Cosmo DeNicola—cosmodenicola.com

Jim Harbaugh—enthusiasmunknowntomankind.com

Mariel Hemingway—marielhemingway.com

Helie Lee—helielee.com

Colonel Tom Manion— travismanion.org

Heather Mitts Feeley—heathermitts.com & ceresplatinumgroup.com

Ken Mok—foxmovies.com/movies/joy

JR Ridinger—beingjrridinger.com

Brian Rutenberg—brianrutenbergart.com

Coach Dick Vermeil—vermeilwines.com

SUPPLEMENT RECOMMENDATIONS:

Isotonix—*isotonix.com/dennisfranks*

TLSSlim—*tlsslim.com/dennisfranks*

10 TIME-SAVING, MIND-FOCUSING APPS

1. **Slack**—Real time messaging to your team.

2. **Tweetdeck**—Organize and time your tweets.

3. **Boomerang for Gmail**—Reach out when the timing's right.

4. **Focus Booster**—Get in the zone: track productivity and analyze your day.

5. **Sanebox**—Separate important emails and create daily digest summaries of others.

6. **Dropbox**—Managing files & folders made easy.

7. **Evernote**—Save text, image, and video files.

8. **Goals On Track**— Set goals, create a dream board.

9. **1-3-5 List**—Prioritize your day quickly.

10. **Wunderlist**—Master to-do list creator.

DENNIS'S SAMPLE WORKOUTS

Plan #1 — Strength and Endurance

Battling Ropes Alt Waves — 3 X 20 reps

Feet Elevated Push-Ups —3 x 15 reps

Sled Pushes — 3 x 40 yds. @90 lbs.

Standing Barbell Overhead Press — 3 x 12 @65 lbs.

Medicine Ball Slams — 3 x 20 reps w/20 lb. med ball

TRX Rows — 3 x 15 reps

Explosive sit-ups — 20 reps w/20 lb. med ball

Russian Twists — 20 reps w/20 lb. med ball

Plank— 60 secs.

Plan #2 — Strength and Stability

Tire Flips-(275 lbs.) — 3 x 8 reps

TRX Single Leg Reverse Lunges — 3 x 15 reps each

Sledge Hammer Slams — 3 x 20 reps

Walk-Outs to Push Up — 3 x 10 reps

Farmers Carry (Suitcase carry) — 3 x 40 yds. w/24 K (52.8 lbs.) KB's

Squats — 3 x 15 reps w/155 lbs.

Bodyweight Single Leg Step-ups — 3 x 15 reps (18" step)

Alternating Reaches — 3 x 20 reps

Med Ball Pikes — 3 x 15 reps

Anti-Rotational Press — 3 x 20 reps (each side)

Plan #3 — Strength

Barbell Bench Press — 3 x 15 @135 lbs.

Lat Pulldown — 3 x 15@100 lbs. (2:2:2 tempo) *

Single Arm Standing Cable Row — 3 x 15(e)@85 lbs.

DB Lateral Raise — 3 x 15@20 lbs.

DB Squat/Bicep Hammer Curl — 3 x 15@25 lbs.

Walkover Push-ups — 3 x 20

KB Swings — 3 x 20 w/24K

Chin-Ups — 5 x 5

Core Routine

Hanging Knee Raises — 3 x 15

Side Planks — 3 x 25 secs (e)

Elephant Walks — 3 x 15

All exercises are performed as a superset followed by a 60-yard jog between sets.

(0:0:0)-Relates to tempo-x seconds down, x seconds hold, x seconds release.

(e)-"Each"

VINCE'S SAMPLE WORKOUT:

20 minutes of cardio at target heart rate

2 minutes of cardio to get to back to target heart rate

20 reps of lat pulldowns followed by 20 reps of bench press

2 minutes of cardio to get to target heart rate

20 reps of curls followed by 20 reps of triceps extension

2 minutes of cardio to get to target heart rate

20 reps of leg extension followed by 20 reps of leg curls

2 minutes of cardio to get to target heart rate

20 reps of rowing followed by 20 reps of overhead press

2 minutes of cardio to get to target heart rate

25 crunches (rest for 30 seconds) do 25 more crunches

Cool down with light cardio moves and stretching

ENDNOTES

1 Cook, Gareth. "The Science of Healing Thoughts." Scientific American, Scientific American , 19 Jan. 2016, www.scientificamerican.com/article/the-science-of-healing-thoughts/.

2 Sood, Amit. The Mayo Clinic guide to stress-free living. Cambridge, MA: Da Capo Press/ Lifelong Books, 2013.

3 Parkinson, Cyril. "Parkinson's Law." The Economist, November 19, 1955. Accessed October 8, 2017. http://www.economist.com/node/14116121.

4 Lemle, Russell B. "How Threat Emotions Cause Us To Misread Our Partner." Psychology Today. March 24, 2012. Accessed November 03, 2017. https://www.psychologytoday.com/ blog/me-first-we-first/201203/how-threat-emotions-cause-us-misread-our-partner-4.

5 European Hydration Institute. "Dehydrated drivers make the same number of mistakes as drunk drivers." April | 54-Dehydrated-Drivers | Loughborough University. Accessed November 03, 2017. http://www.lboro.ac.uk/media-centre/press-releases/2015/april/54-dehydrated-drivers.html.

6 American College of Sports Medicine. Selecting and Effectively Using Hydration for Fitness. American College of Sports Medicine. https://www.acsm.org/docs/brochures/ selecting-and-effectively-using-hydration-for-fitness.pdf.

7 T. H. Chan School of Public Health. "Nutrition Insurance Policy: A Daily Multivitamin." The Nutrition Source. October 10, 2014. Accessed November 03, 2017. https://www.hsph. harvard.edu/nutritionsource/multivitamin/.

8 American Heart Association. "Fish and Omega-3 Fatty Acids." Heart.org. Accessed November 03, 2017. http://www.heart.org/HEARTORG/HealthyLiving/HealthyEating/ HealthyDietGoals/Fish-and-Omega-3-Fatty-Acids_UCM_303248_Article.jsp#. WfxqjmhSxPZ.

9 Hunninghake, Ron , MD. "Vitamins D3 and K2 - The Dynamic Duo." Riordan Clinic. October 07, 2013. Accessed November 03, 2017. https://riordanclinic.org/2013/10/ vitamins-d3-and-k2-the-dynamic-duo/.

10 Ergotron. "New Survey: To Sit or Stand? Almost 70% of Full Time American Workers Hate Sitting, but They do it all Day Every Day." PR Newswire: news distribution, targeting and monitoring. July 17, 2013. Accessed November 03, 2017. https://www.prnewswire.com/ news-releases/new-survey-to-sit-or-stand-almost-70-of-full-time-american-workers-hate-sitting-but-they-do-it-all-day-every-day-215804771.html.

11 CBS News. "Too much sitting raises risk of death, even if you exercise." CBS News. January 19, 2015. Accessed November 03, 2017. https://www.cbsnews.com/news/too-much-sitting-raises-risk-of-death-even-if-you-exercise/.